Focus in High School Mathematics:
Reasoning and Sense Making in Statistics and Probability

by

J. Michael Shaughnessy
Portland State University
Portland, Oregon

Beth Chance
California Polytechnic State University
San Luis Obispo, California

Henry Kranendonk
Milwaukee Public Schools
Milwaukee, Wisconsin

NATIONAL COUNCIL OF
TEACHERS OF MATHEMATICS

Copyright © 2009 by
The National Council of Teachers of Mathematics, Inc.
1906 Association Drive, Reston, VA 20191-1502
(703) 620-9840; (800) 235-7566; www.nctm.org
All rights reserved

Third printing 2012

Library of Congress Cataloging-in-Publication Data

Shaughnessy, Michael, 1946-
  Focus in high school mathematics : reasoning and sense making
in statistics and probability / by J. Michael Shaughnessy,
Beth Chance, Henry Kranendonk.
      p. cm.
  A companion topic focus book to Focus in high school mathematics :
reasoning and sense making.
  Includes bibliographical references.
  ISBN 978-0-87353-642-4 (alk. paper)
  1. Statistics—Study and teaching (Secondary)—United States. 2.
Curriculum planning—United States. I. Chance, Beth L. II. Kranendonk,
Henry. III. National Council of Teachers of Mathematics. IV. Title. V.
Title: Statistics and probability.

  QA276.18.S527 2009
  519.5071'273—dc22

                          2009036323

The National Council of Teachers of Mathematics is a public voice of
mathematics education, supporting teachers to ensure equitable mathematics
learning of the highest quality for all students through vision, leadership,
professional development, and research.

Printed in the United States of America

Table of Contents

Preface

Focus in High School Mathematics: Reasoning and Sense Making (NCTM 2009) captures the direction for high school mathematics for students in the twenty-first century:

> Reasoning and sense making should occur in every mathematics classroom every day. In such an environment, teachers and students ask and answer such questions as "What's going on here?" and "Why do you think that?" Addressing reasoning and sense making does not need to be an extra burden for teachers struggling with students who are having a difficult time just learning the procedures. On the contrary, the structure that reasoning brings forms a vital support for understanding and continued learning. Currently, many students have difficulty because they find mathematics meaningless…. With purposeful attention and planning, teachers can hold all students in every high school mathematics classroom accountable for personally engaging in reasoning and sense making, and thus lead students to experience reasoning for themselves rather than merely observe it. (NCTM 2009, pp. 5–6)

This new publication urges a refocusing of the high school mathematics curriculum on reasoning and sense making, building on the guidelines for teaching and learning mathematics advocated by NCTM in *Principles and Standards for School Mathematics* (NCTM 2000). *Focus in High School Mathematics: Reasoning and Sense Making* makes the case that reasoning and sense making must reside at the core of all mathematics learning and instruction, at all grades. Moving forward from *Curriculum Focal Points for Prekindergarten through Grade 8 Mathematics* (NCTM 2006), *Focus in High School Mathematics: Reasoning and Sense Making* also addresses the need for the continuation of a coherent and well-articulated mathematics curriculum at the high school level.

The underlying principles of *Focus in High School Mathematics: Reasoning and Sense Making* are "reasoning habits" that should develop across the curriculum, along with "key elements" organized around five content strands. The book provides a group of examples that illustrate how these principles might play out in the classroom. Historically, NCTM has provided supplementary materials to accompany major publications that present official positions of the Council (e.g., the Teaching with Curriculum Focal Points series for *Curriculum Focal Points for Prekindergarten through Grade 8 Mathematics,* the Navigations Series for *Principles and Standards for School Mathematics*, the Addenda Series for *Curriculum and Evaluation Standards for School Mathematics* [NCTM 1989]). In keeping with this tradition, a series of supplementary books, Focus in High School Mathematics, provides additional guidance for ensuring that reasoning and sense making are part of the mathematics experiences of all high school students every day.

This series is intended for secondary mathematics teachers, curriculum specialists, mathematics supervisors, district administrators, and mathematics teacher educators. *Focus in High School Mathematics: Reasoning and Sense Making* underscores the critical role of the Process Standards outlined in *Principles and Standards* and provides a foundation for achieving the principal goals for the mathematical experiences of all secondary school students. Each volume in the Focus in High School Mathematics series presents detailed examples of worthwhile mathematical tasks, along with follow-up discussion. The examples and discussions are intended to help classroom teachers understand what it means to promote sense making and to find ways to increase it in their classrooms. The material could also be used as classroom cases in professional development. In addition, supervisors, curriculum specialists, and administrators might use the examples and discussions to catalyze conversations about shifts in the high school mathematics curriculum to bring them into alignment with the goals of *Focus in High School Mathematics: Reasoning and Sense Making.*

Although the books in the series focus on a particular content strand from *Principles and Standards* (e.g., geometry and measurement, algebra, statistics and probability), they are not intended to outline a curriculum for a particular content area. In fact, many of the examples in the books point to potential connections across content areas.

The authors of the present volume, *Focus in High School Mathematics: Reasoning and Sense Making in Statistics and Probability,* extend sincere thanks to those who reviewed the manuscript at various stages and offered valuable suggestions:

Gary D. Kader, Appalachian State University, Boone, North Carolina

Christine A. Franklin, University of Georgia, Athens, Georgia

Fred Rectanus, Portland Public Schools and Teachers Development Group, Portland, Oregon

Jennifer Noll, Portland State University, Portland, Oregon

General Introduction to the Focus in High School Mathematics Series

Focus in High School Mathematics: Reasoning and Sense Making addresses the need for reasoning to play a larger role in high school mathematics:

> A focus on reasoning and sense making, when developed in the context of strong content, will ensure that students can accurately carry out mathematical procedures, understand why those procedures work, and know how they might be used and their results interpreted…. Such a focus on reasoning and sense making will produce citizens who make informed and reasoned decisions, including quantitatively sophisticated choices about their personal finances, about which public policies deserve their support, and about which insurance or health plans to select. It will also produce workers who can satisfy the increased mathematical needs in professional areas ranging from health care to small business to digital technology. (NCTM 2009, p. 3)

Focus in High School Mathematics: Reasoning and Sense Making provides an outline for how reasoning and sense making might play out in core topic areas of the high school curriculum: numbers and measurement, algebra, geometry, and statistics and probability. The topics and examples contained in this publication and the supporting volumes do not represent an exhaustive list of topics that should be covered in any particular course or curriculum. The examples are meant to illustrate reasoning habits that all students at a variety of grade levels should know by the time they complete high school. As such, they provide multiple entry points for the students and, where appropriate, emphasize connections between several areas of mathematics. The discussions point to key teaching strategies that foster the development of reasoning and sense making. The strategies should be viewed as general and not tied to the particular context or task.

Most teachers and teacher educators would probably nod in agreement that reasoning and sense making are important to consider in the mathematical experiences of their students. However, the purpose of *Focus in High School Mathematics: Reasoning and Sense Making* and the Focus in High School Mathematics series is to highlight these as major goals of the study of secondary mathematics. Although reasoning and sense making may have been a part of secondary mathematics teaching and learning in the past, they are certainly worthy of being discussed in greater depth, and becoming a primary focus of our secondary mathematics teaching, in classrooms today. Therefore, with this shift in emphasis, it is important for NCTM to provide thoughtful examples of worthwhile tasks that can be pursued at a number of levels.

The Role of Teaching

Often, high school mathematics teaching in the United States and Canada has been characterized by two main classroom activities; teachers share information, such as definitions of new terms and procedures for solving mathematics problems, and then students practice and perhaps discuss results of those procedures. Although these activities are important, such practices can lead to learning that is devoid of reasoning and sense making. By contrast, NCTM strongly supports a view of mathematics teaching and learning that focuses on reasoning, as described in *Mathematics Teaching Today* (NCTM 2007): "Teachers … must shift their perspectives about teaching from that of a process of delivering information to that of a process of facilitating students' sense making about mathematics" (p. 5).

A shift of perspective to one that views reasoning and sense making as primary goals for students' learning of mathematics will lead to a shift in choices made by the classroom teacher. For example, the teacher will choose tasks that allow students to see the need for sense making and provide opportunities for them to demonstrate their reasoning processes. Such tasks should also help students build on their informal knowledge of mathematics and see the logical connections with other areas of mathematics that they have learned. This shift may require changes in the structure of the classroom setting so that students are challenged and encouraged to explore mathematical situations both collaboratively and independently. Students should be expected to make conjectures and develop arguments to support them, connecting earlier knowledge with newly acquired knowledge.

As students are investigating and shaping ideas, they should have opportunities to interact directly and openly with one another and with the teacher. More details about the teacher's and students' roles in the classroom can be found in chapter 1, "Standards for Teaching and Learning," of *Mathematics Teaching Today*, which includes Standards describing characteristics of *worthwhile mathematical tasks* (Standard 3), components of a productive classroom *learning environment* (Standard 4), and suggestions for orchestrating mathematical *discourse* (Standard 5). The Focus in High School Mathematics series provides tasks, examples, and classroom vignettes that illustrate how a teacher might choose tasks and orchestrate classroom discourse to capitalize on student reasoning and promote sense making.

The Role of Technology

Technology is integrated into the examples in these books in a strategic manner to enrich opportunities for students' reasoning and sense making. The power of recent technological tools (e.g., computer algebra systems, dynamic geometry software, and dynamic data representation tools) to enhance reasoning and sense making in mathematics is so great that it would be remiss to omit them from these volumes.

Increasingly, technology is an integral part of society and the research that is conducted in the majority of mathematics-related fields. We support the philosophy of *Focus in High School Mathematics: Reasoning and Sense Making* that "students can be challenged to take responsibility for deciding which tool might be useful in a given situation when they are allowed to choose from a menu of mathematical tools that includes technology. Students who have regular opportunities to discuss and reflect on how a technological tool is used effectively will be less apt to use technology as a crutch" (p. 14). The Focus in High School Mathematics series provides examples that show students using technology to reduce computational overhead, but the books also illustrate the use of technology in experimenting with mathematical objects and modeling mathematical structures.

The Focus in High School Mathematics Series

Focus in High School Mathematics: Reasoning and Sense Making underscores the need to refocus the high school mathematics curriculum on reasoning and sense making. Companion books provide further insights into how these ways of thinking might develop in three major areas of content in high school mathematics:

- *Focus in High School Mathematics: Reasoning and Sense Making in Algebra*
- *Focus in High School Mathematics: Reasoning and Sense Making in Geometry*
- *Focus in High School Mathematics: Reasoning and Sense Making in Statistics and Probability*

The strand on reasoning and sense making with numbers and measurement discussed in *Focus in High School Mathematics: Reasoning and Sense Making* receives primary attention in *Focus in High School Mathematics: Reasoning and Sense Making in Geometry,* but aspects of this strand are also addressed in the other two content books.

Reasoning Habits

To detail what mathematical reasoning and sense making should look like across the high school curriculum, *Focus in High School Mathematics: Reasoning and Sense Making* provides a list of "reasoning habits." The intent is not to present a new list of topics to be added to the high school curriculum: "Approaching the list as a new set of topics to be taught in an already crowded curriculum is not likely to have the desired effect. Instead, attention to reasoning habits needs to be integrated within the curriculum to ensure that students both understand and can use what they are taught" (p. 9). The reasoning habits are described and illustrated in the examples throughout the companion books in the Focus in High School Mathematics series.

Key Elements

Focus in High School Mathematics: Reasoning and Sense Making identifies "key elements" for each of the strands. These key elements are intended to provide "a lens through which to view the potential of high school programs for promoting mathematical reasoning and sense making" (p. 18).

Content Expectations

As *Focus in High School Mathematics: Reasoning and Sense Making* suggests, readers wishing for more detailed content recommendations should refer to chapter 7, "Standards for Grades 9–12," of *Principles and Standards for School Mathematics* (NCTM 2000). However, for the readers' convenience, each companion volume shows the grades 9–12 expectations of the relevant Standard (Algebra, Geometry, or Data Analysis and Probability) in the appendix, along with the grades 9–12 expectations for the Number and Operations and the Measurement Standards, which are addressed by all three volumes.

Introduction
to *Focus in High School Mathematics: Reasoning and Sense Making in Statistics and Probability*

Statistics is increasingly recognized as a critical area for students' success in dealing with the requirements of citizenship, employment, and continuing education (Franklin et al. 2007; College Board 2006, 2007; American Diploma Project 2004). Consequently, the development of statistical reasoning must be a high priority for school mathematics. Preparing high school graduates with the ability to make sense of data, and with the capacity to reason with and about statistics, requires that students be engaged in meaningful activities involving data and chance from prekindergarten through grade 12. This will allow students in their secondary years to have the opportunity to develop the critical reasoning skills that will be essential for dealing with data and statistical claims in their future employment and their roles as citizens of our nation.

In our increasingly data-intensive world, statistics is one of the most important areas of the mathematical sciences for helping students make sense of the information all around them, as well as for preparing them for further study in a variety of disciplines (e.g., the health sciences, the social sciences, and environmental science) in which statistics is a fundamental tool for advancing knowledge. Achieving competence according to the Standards set forth in *Principles and Standards for School Mathematics* (NCTM 2000) depends on a thorough and deep understanding of the foundations of statistics and probability and of the connections between statistics and probability. Statistical reasoning is also inherently different from mathematical reasoning, and effective development of it requires distinct exercises and experiences. In particular, statistical reasoning centers on a *focus on making sense of and reasoning about variation in data*.

The need for statistics arises from "the omnipresence of variability" in data (Cobb and Moore 1997, p. 801), and statistical reasoning uses a combination of ideas from both data and chance in seeking to understand and explain the variability. The goal is not only to solve problems in the presence of variation, but also to obtain a measure of how much the variation might affect the solution. This process provides a framework for teaching and learning statistics in the schools, and meaningful tasks that employ this process should permeate the statistical education of our students.

According to *Principles and Standards* and the American Statistical Association's report *Guidelines for Assessment and Instruction in Statistics Education* (GAISE) (Franklin et al. 2007), the investigative process of a statistical study takes students through four fundamental steps or stages:

1. **Formulating** a question (or questions) that can be addressed with data
2. **Designing and employing** a plan for collecting data
3. **Analyzing and summarizing** the data
4. **Interpreting** the results from the analysis, and answering the question on the basis of the data

As also illustrated by the PPDAC (Problem, Plan, Data, Analysis, Conclusion) cycle (Wild and Pfannkuch 1999), students need to be able to understand and define a statistical question; to consider appropriate data collection plans that will yield meaningful data; to critique the validity and relevance of available data; to include what to measure and how to measure it. Students also need to recognize the study design; to be aware of issues in data management and data cleaning; to construct illuminating numerical and graphical summaries of data; to look for patterns, build predictive models and generate hypotheses; to interpret the results, relate them to the context, draw appropriate conclusions, generate new questions, and communicate their results to others within the context of a problem (e.g., Frankcom 2008). Notions such as distribution, center, spread, association, uncertainty, randomness, sampling, and statistical experiments are foundational concepts underlying the development of statistical reasoning.

This book explores several episodes that provide a glimpse of teachers' attempts to deepen students' statistical reasoning at different stages. Teachers might encourage students at an early stage to be "data detectives," looking for patterns in the data and considering what stories are to be found in them. Questions such as "What do we notice; what do we wonder about?" and "What questions might we pose for a future statistical study?" help to develop data-detective skills. Students need to become accustomed to looking at and linking different representations of data (tables, graphs, summaries), making comparisons, and considering trends and predictions that can be supported by the data, as well as attending to the constant interplay between the data and the context in which the data arise. Students should constantly be considering informal inferences that they can make from the data, and later work can introduce them to the more formal logic of inferential reasoning. For teachers, an overarching goal in all of this work is developing in students a healthy skepticism about published studies. Students need to be aware of the critical elements that are essential in a statistical investigation, either in the development of a new study or in the presentation of a past study.

Key Elements of Statistical Reasoning

As identified in *Focus in High School Mathematics: Reasoning and Sense Making* (NCTM 2009), the key elements for reasoning and sense making with statistics and probability are as follows:

- *Analyzing data.* Gaining insight about a solution to a statistics research question by collecting data and describing features of the data using graphical and tabular representations and numerical summaries.

- *Modeling distributions.* Developing probability models to describe long-run behavior of observations of a random variable.

- *Connecting statistics and probability.* Recognizing variability as an essential focus of statistics and understanding the role of probability in statistical reasoning to make decisions under uncertainty.

- *Interpreting designed statistical studies.* Drawing appropriate conclusions from the data and interpreting results from designed statistical studies using statistical inference.

Each chapter presented in this book deals in detail with one or more of these key elements of statistical reasoning. The first three chapters focus more on data analysis, and the last three chapters are more involved with interpreting statistical studies and connecting probability distributions with statistics. In addition to these key elements, certain aspects of the reasoning habits are particularly evident in statistical thinking.

Habits of Mind in Statistical Thinking

Focus in High School Mathematics: Reasoning and Sense Making identifies a set of habits of mind that are critical in mathematical reasoning. This companion volume identifies specific habits of mind that are of particular importance in statistical reasoning (see table 0.1).

Table 0.1
Habits of Mind in Reasoning and Sense Making in Statistics and Probability

---

Analyzing a problem

Looking for patterns and relationships by—

- describing overall patterns in data;
- analyzing and explaining variation;
- looking for hidden structure in the data;
- making preliminary deductions and conjectures.

Implementing a strategy

Selecting representations or procedures by—

- choosing and critiquing data collection strategies based on the question;
- creating meaningful graphical representations and numerical summaries;
- considering the random mechanisms behind the data;
- choosing a model;
- drawing conclusions beyond the data.

Monitoring one's progress

Evaluating a chosen strategy by—

- comparing various graphical and numerical representations;
- comparing various interpretations of the data;
- evaluating the consistency of an observation with a model;
- questioning whether the observations make sense within the problem context;
- evaluating the consistency of different components of the analysis;
- applying the iterative statistical process to the investigation.

Seeking and using connections

Connecting different representations by—

- noticing connections in a variety of graphical and numerical representations;
- identifying common components of analyses (e.g., standardization);
- understanding the sensitivity of an analysis to various components;
- connecting conclusions and interpretations to the context.

Reflecting on one's solutions

Checking the reasonableness of an answer by—

- considering and evaluating alternative explanations;
- understanding the allowable scope of conclusions;
- determining whether a conclusion based on the data is plausible;
- justifying or validating the solution or conclusion by using inferential reasoning;
- analyzing and accounting for variability;
- looking for connections between the data and the context.

Many of these statistical subthemes within the reasoning habits are related to the constant interplay between the data and the context in which the data arises. In this respect, statistical reasoning differs from mathematical reasoning because there is *always* a context to be considered in statistics.

The Content and Flow of This Book

Each of the six chapters in this book presents a statistical task that secondary mathematics and statistics students can carry out. The purpose of the investigations as well as the key elements and habits of mind addressed in the tasks are identified near the beginning of the initial discussion in each chapter. The discussion also addresses the reason that the data or question would be of interest, the important statistical ideas in the investigation, and the type of study and type of data involved. Examples of students' reasoning are threaded throughout the presentation of each investigation.

Conversation between the authors and the readers occurs simultaneously at three levels: (1) in the task or investigation itself, along with suggestions for how to carry it out with students; (2) in examples of students' reasoning or students' responses at various points while they are doing the statistics; and (3) in discussions with and notes to teachers, explaining decisions to do things in certain ways or offering suggestions for what teachers should expect when they do the tasks with students in their classrooms. The authors have attempted to be very clear about why certain questions are posed and why students might reason in certain ways in these statistical investigations.

The investigations involve analyzing data sets, constructing and comparing various graphical representations of data, gathering data from simulations and constructing randomization distributions, analyzing a report on a statistical study, and comparing data sets and testing for differences between or among them. Brief descriptions follow of the investigations by chapter:

1. **Country data.** Students compare population age across countries. This investigation is a data analysis activity involving entire census data sets. Students focus on uncovering and explaining patterns in the data and differences among countries.

2. **Old Faithful.** Students examine and represent data from the Old Faithful geyser. Like the investigation in chapter 1, this investigation is also primarily a data analysis activity, but it allows students to work with samples of data drawn over time. Students focus on variation in inter-eruption times within and between years and decide how that variation might be characterized and explained.

3. **Olympic times.** Students investigate whether race times for men and women will coincide someday. This investigation again focuses on census data—all the data on Olympic times for the 200-meter dash for both men and women. This data analysis investigation involves bivariate data collected over time. Students develop predictive models and consider plausible conjectures about future performance.

4. **Coffee drinking.** Students consider the gender of customers at the local coffee shop: are there more females than males? This investigation begins with students designing a data collection plan for sampling from a larger population. Once data are collected, the students consider the plausibility of various values of the population proportion by using simulations of sampling distributions.

5. **Meaningful words.** Students analyze memory comparisons for meaningful versus nonsense words. In this analysis of a statistical study focused on comparing two groups on a quantitative variable, students use simulation tools to help determine whether the difference in the performance of two groups is larger than they would expect from chance variation.

6. **Soda and heart disease.** Does evidence support a link between soft drink consumption and a metabolic syndrome that leads to heart disease? In this investigation, students examine the results of an actual statistical study and then critique and evaluate the study as it was presented in the news media.

In presenting each of these investigations, we try to include the spectrum of student reasoning that we have experienced in our own classrooms, from initial, basic comments and observations up through fairly sophisticated types of reasoning that can and do occur with more experienced students. Each investigation can be carried much further than we have been able to detail in this short book, so we have provided further questions or extensions for each of the six activities.

We sincerely hope that readers of this book will find these sample pieces helpful in eliciting and developing their own students' reasoning and sense making in statistics. When you have finished reading the book—and perhaps you and your students have completed its investigations—take a look forward in your school mathematics program and try to identify opportunities to highlight and embed student reasoning and sense making in statistical settings.

Make it a habit to seek such opportunities. Reasoning and sense making are not activities that we should engage our students in doing just occasionally, here and there in the curriculum. Instead, they should play important roles at the beginning, middle, and end of everything that we do with our students in all of their mathematics, and we should provide them with experiences that allow them to share their reasoning every day, within every topic, task, or concept that we address with them. Perhaps the reasoning pieces in this book can provide a blueprint to help teachers incorporate reasoning and sense making in all their work with their students in statistics and probability.

Chapter 1

Country Data—A Look at Some Census Data

This chapter attempts to capture the initial stages of reasoning with data for students who have limited experiences with authentic data. In the tasks, the students work with data that are from entire populations, rather than samples collected from a population. The distinction between populations and samples is a critical one for students to address when reasoning about data and making sense of statistical studies.

The Context

The tasks in this chapter ask students to reason about population data from three countries, using tables and then subsequent representations consisting of histograms and box plots. By examining these various representations of the same data, students begin to compare countries by using the median ages, the percentage of people in various age categories (e.g., "older people," teenagers), and the general shape of the visual representations. By using census data, students can focus more directly on uncovering and describing patterns in distributions—skills that should not be overlooked. Using percentages to compare populations effectively requires students to demonstrate their reasoning beyond the simple computational skills that they might have mastered, and thus leads them to proportional reasoning. This chapter also attempts to demonstrate how students might learn to interpret data in the process of exploring the constant interplay between data and context. For example, in what way are the differences in the distribution of the countries' populations related to economic or cultural differences that might not be directly evident from the data itself? Table 1.1 identifies the key element and summarizes the general reasoning habits and the specific statistical reasoning habits of mind that are involved in this investigation.

Table 1.1
Key Element and Habits of Mind in the Country Investigation

Key Element: Analyzing Data

Habits of Mind

Analyzing a problem

Looking for patterns and relationships by—
* describing overall patterns in the data;

7

Table 1.1.—*Continued*

- looking for hidden structure in the data;
- making preliminary deductions and conjectures.

Monitoring one's progress

Evaluating a chosen strategy by—
- comparing various graphical and numerical representations;
- evaluating the consistency of different components of the analysis.

Seeking and using connections

Connecting different representations by—
- noticing connections in a variety of graphical and numerical representations;
- connecting conclusions and interpretations to the context.

Reflecting on one's solutions

Checking the reasonableness of an answer by—
- justifying or validating the solution or conclusion by using inferential reasoning;
- determining whether a conclusion based on the data is plausible.

Introduction to the Task

In 1986, students at Rufus King High School in Milwaukee, Wisconsin, were able to establish an e-mail exchange with students at the International Baccalaureate School in Nairobi, Kenya. The opportunity to make a direct connection with students from another country was a novel and exciting development for many students in 1986. Today, opportunities to communicate with students around the world abound as students readily use text messaging, social networking, blogging, and numerous other communication tools.

For students to communicate effectively with students from other countries, they need to understand and make sense of the challenges faced by the people in these countries and consider whether or not those challenges are similar to or different from those faced in their own country. This investigation provides students with several opportunities to explore either entire populations or samples from such populations. Making sense of the population data involves understanding why, where, and how the data were collected. This information provides a background for the interpretation of the data.

In the tasks that follow, students will explore data on the ages of people in three countries—the United States, Japan, and Kenya. The data are summarized in tables, histograms, and box plots. Using percentages, ratios, and other numerical summaries of the data, students learn how to answer the question of how population data can be used to compare countries. Students begin to see how countries differ and how these differences generate more questions and more data.

The task presented to students

The students at Rufus King High School began their investigation by looking at census data on the ages of the population of the United States from data sets provided by the Census Bureau (http://www.census.gov). Data from the United States Census Bureau offer numerous summaries of the U.S. population and the populations of other countries of the world as part of an international database (IDB) maintained and easily accessible at the Census Bureau Web site. Census data are very important in understanding the United States and other countries. In fact, the Constitution of the United States mandates that a census of the people in the country be conducted at least once every ten years.

The first summary of data in this investigation appears in table 1.2. The table provides students with information about the U.S. population in age bands in the year 2000.

Table 1.2
Population of the United States in 2000

Five-year age groups	Number of people (in thousands)
Under 5 years	19,919
5 to 9 years	20,853
10 to 14 years	20,693
15 to 19 years	20,062
20 to 24 years	19,172
25 to 29 years	19,610
30 to 34 years	20,887
35 to 39 years	22,976
40 to 44 years	22,846
45 to 49 years	20,516
50 to 54 years	17,661
55 to 59 years	13,684
60 to 64 years	10,911
65 to 69 years	9,548
70 to 74 years	8,911
75 to 79 years	7,467
80 to 84 years	5,024
85 to 89 years	2,699
90 to 94 years	1,077
95 to 99 years	303
Total	284,819

Note to Teachers

You can lead a discussion to introduce the population data for the United States. Before presenting the data to students, you might ask them to define what a census is, how it differs from a sample, and why they think a census once every ten years was regarded as so important that it was included in the Constitution of the United States.

Discussion among Students and the Teacher

The following dialogue reflects the development of the students' reasoning about the investigation.

Initial student reasoning

Teacher: Our first goal in this investigation is to describe the distribution of ages in the U.S. population in 2000. The number of people in each age category is in thousands. Therefore, the approximate number of people under 5 years old in 2000 is 19,919,000, or nearly 20 million people. The approximate number of people who are 35 to 39 years old is 22,976,000, or nearly 23 million people. Using the estimated number of people in the table, how would you describe this distribution? Do you notice any trends in the data?

Student A: Would I look for a pattern?

Student B: There is a general pattern, because the population goes up and down in the first part of the table. There is a peak value at the 35–39 year-old age range, and then it goes steadily down.

Teacher: What would that tell us about the ages of the U.S. population in 2000?

Student A: The country had fewer people in the youngest ages and the oldest ages. Most of the people were in the middle of the age ranges in the year 2000.

Teacher: Instead of providing a count for each age group, is there another way that we can summarize the age distribution?

Student B: There were large increases and decreases in the values of numbers as I moved through the age categories. The changes were in some cases just a few thousand people to more than a couple million people in some categories. What if we changed each category to a percent of the total population?

Teacher: Let's add some percentage columns [*see table 1.3*] and then discuss the results again.

Table 1.3
Percentage Breakdown of U.S. Population in Five-Year Age Groups

Five-year age groups	Number of people (in thousands)	Percent of the total population	Cumulative percent
Under 5 years	19,919	6.99%	6.99%
5 to 9 years	20,853	7.32%	14.31%
10 to 14 years	20,693	7.27%	21.58%
15 to 19 years	20,062	7.04%	28.62%
20 to 24 years	19,172	6.73%	35.35%
25 to 29 years	19,610	6.89%	42.24%
30 to 34 years	20,887	7.33%	49.57%
35 to 39 years	22,976	8.07%	57.64%
40 to 44 years	22,846	8.02%	65.66%
45 to 49 years	20,516	7.20%	72.86%
50 to 54 years	17,661	6.20%	79.06%
55 to 59 years	13,684	4.80%	83.86%

Table 1.3—*Continued*

Five-year age groups	Number of people (in thousands)	Percent of the total population	Cumulative percent
60 to 64 years	10,911	3.83%	87.69%
65 to 69 years	9,548	3.35%	91.04%
70 to 74 years	8,911	3.13%	94.17%
75 to 79 years	7,467	2.62%	96.79%
80 to 84 years	5,024	1.76%	98.55%
85 to 89 years	2,699	0.95%	99.5%
90 to 94 years	1,077	0.38%	99.88%
95 to 99 years	303	0.11%	99.99%

Teacher: With the percentages of each age category added to the table, what else could we summarize about the population?

Student A: As I indicated before, the percentage of each category bounces around but peaks at the 35–39 age category, and then goes down. There are big percentage differences starting at 50- to 54-year-olds, from 6.2% of the population to 4.8% in the 55- to 59-year-olds.

Teacher: What might be the explanation for these differences?

Student B: Maybe there were fewer people born 55 to 59 years ago? Wouldn't the percentage of the people in that age category be somewhat based on the number of people born 55 to 59 years ago?

Student A: And clearly, the smaller percentages of people in the older age categories would also indicate that more people probably died even if the age category was the same as the values of the younger ages.

Teacher: A lot of your observations would be clearer if we had data from other years. For example, maybe a similar table from 1950 or earlier would answer some of your questions. Before looking at some other data sets, use these summaries of the data to make three statements that tell us something about the distribution of ages for the population of the United States in 2000.

Student A: The percentage of people 9 years and younger was 14.31%. If I start at the older end of the table, the percentage of people 65 and older was 12.3%. I find these two categories interesting to compare—the children and the older people—they are nearly the same percentage of the population.

Student B: I tried to group the population in thirds. I could not make it come out to exactly 33.3%, however, I found that 35.35% were 0 to 24 years old, 30.1% were 25 to 44 years old, and 34.33% were 45 to 99 years old. Approximately two-thirds of the population in 2000 was younger than 44 years old.

Student C: You could also say that two-thirds of the population was 25 and older.

Teacher: We are beginning to see a description of the population based on a summary of the data.

Data from other countries

Teacher: Suppose that we look at the frequency tables of some other countries—say, Japan and Kenya in 2000 [*see table 1.4*], and compare their populations with the U.S. population. What observations can we make?

Student A: Kenya has a very consistent pattern—each age category has a smaller percentage of the total population than the one before.

Student B: If you compare percentages from one age group to the next, the percentages are very different for each country. Japan has the largest percentage of people in the 50- to 54-year-old category, while Kenya has the largest percentage in the "under 5" category. I think Japan has a larger percentage of its people older than either the USA or Kenya.

Student C: Nearly one-third—30.22%—of the people in Kenya were under 10 years old in 2000.

Student B: A little over one-third of the people in Japan were under 30 years old. In Kenya, nearly 80% of the people were under 30 years old in 2000.

Teacher: Very different descriptions are needed to summarize the population of Japan and Kenya.

Student A: Japan has a much older population, and Kenya, a very young population.

Teacher: Would the differences suggest different challenges for each country?

Student A: Kenya probably has a major challenge in caring for the very young. Japan might have an equal challenge in caring for the older people.

Teacher: To start your summary of each country, let's estimate the median age of the population in each country.

Student B: The median age is the age at which 50% of the population is above this age and about 50% is below. If we use the Cumulative Percent column from our tables, I guess the median age in Kenya to be between 14 years old to 19 years old; in the United States it would be in the range of 34 to 39 years old, and in Japan it would be between 39 to 44 years old.

Table 1.4
Five-Year Population Groups for Kenya and Japan

Five-year age groups	Kenya			Japan			
	Number of people (in thousands)	Percent of the total population	Cumulative percent	Number of people (in thousands)	Percent of the total population	Cumulative percent	Five-year age groups
Under 5	5,082	16.26%	16.26%	6,055	4.77%	4.77%	Under 5
5 to 9	4,362	13.96%	30.22%	5,998	4.72%	9.49%	5 to 9
10 to 14	4,271	13.67%	43.89%	6,544	5.15%	14.64%	10 to 14
15 to 19	3,757	12.02%	55.91%	7,503	5.91%	20.55%	15 to 19
20 to 24	3,088	9.88%	65.79%	8,597	6.77%	27.32%	20 to 24
25 to 29	2,466	7.89%	73.68%	9,924	7.81%	35.13%	25 to 29
30 to 34	1,932	6.18%	79.86%	8,803	6.93%	42.06%	30 to 34
35 to 39	1,560	4.99%	84.85%	8,123	6.40%	48.46%	35 to 39
40 to 44	1,248	3.99%	88.84%	7,797	6.14%	54.60%	40 to 44
45 to 49	993	3.18%	92.02%	8,939	7.04%	61.64%	45 to 49
50 to 54	714	2.28%	94.30%	10,472	8.24%	69.88%	50 to 54
55 to 59	490	1.57%	95.87%	8,726	6.87%	76.75%	55 to 59
60 to 64	423	1.35%	97.22%	7,690	6.05%	82.80%	60 to 64
65 to 69	357	1.14%	98.36%	7,086	5.58%	88.38%	65 to 69
70 to 74	248	0.79%	99.15%	5,870	4.62%	93.00%	70 to 74
75 to 79	150	0.48%	99.63%	4,095	3.22%	96.22%	75 to 79
80 to 84	77	0.25%	99.88%	2,594	2.04%	98.26%	80 to 84
85 to 89	28	0.09%	99.97%	1,518	1.20%	99.46%	85 to 89
90 to 94	7	0.02%	99.99%	564	0.44%	99.90%	90 to 94
95 to 99	1	0.00%	99.99%	123	0.10%	100.00%	95 to 99
Total	31,254			127,021			Total

Population histograms

Teacher: Let's look at histograms for the distributions of ages for these three countries [*see figs. 1.1 and 1.2*]. Note that the identity of the country is missing from these histograms. Can you tell which country is represented by each histogram?

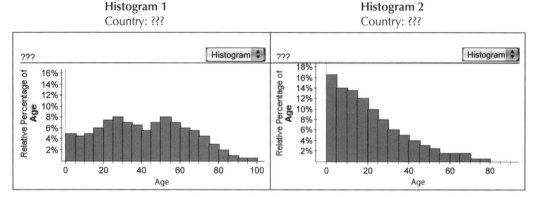

Fig. 1.1. Population histograms for two of the countries

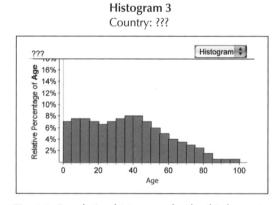

Fig. 1.2. Population histograms for the third country

Student A: The summaries we made from the table are illustrated in the histograms. For example, histogram 2 has the population start out large and decrease for each age category. This was the pattern of Kenya that we summarized from the table.

Student B: Histogram 3 shows that bulge in the middle group of age categories that made up the larger percentage of the population in the United States.

Student C: And histogram 1 indicates a greater percentage of the total population in the age categories of 30 and older, and then again in the 50s. This was the summary we made for Japan.

Student A: The histograms provide a clearer picture of the changes and the patterns we observed in the tables. I think they pretty much show the same summaries of the tables, but the histograms show the data as almost a picture.

Student B: I agree.

Examining box plots

Teacher: Let's look at the populations of the same three countries in 2000, this time summarized with box plots [*see figs. 1.3–1.5*]. Again, the identifications of the countries are missing. Can we match each country with the correct box plot? First of all, have you worked with box plots before?

[*The students indicate that they need help in making sense of the information in a box plot.*]

Box plot 1
Country: ??? (2000)

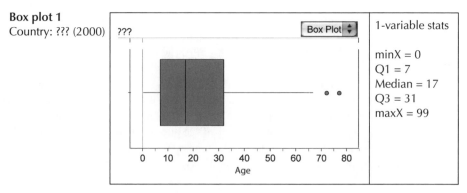

Fig. 1.3. A box plot for the first country

Box plot 2
Country: ??? (2000)

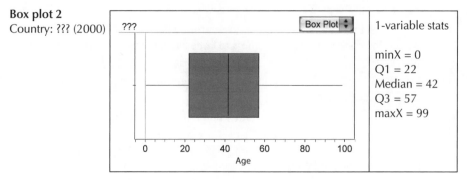

Fig. 1.4. A box plot for the second country

Box plot 3
Country: ??? (2000)

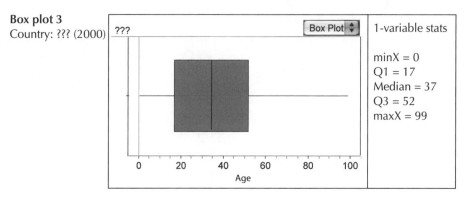

Fig. 1.5. A box plot for the third country

Teacher:	The box plot for a set of data summarizes the data on the basis of five quantities:

1. The minimum value
2. The first quartile (Q1)
3. The median
4. The third quartile (Q3)
5. The maximum value

	These five quantities essentially divide the ordered data into fourths, or quarters. So, looking at the output on the right side of the box plot for the third box plot, you can see that the minimum age is 0, and the first quartile is 17. This means that approximately 25% of the people in that country are between 0 and 17 years old. The interval 0 to 17 is sometimes called the first or lower quarter of the data, whereas *quartile* refers to the numerical value of the edge of that first quarter. In a similar way, the second quarter of the ages is the interval 17 to 37, and approximately 25% of the population is between 17 and 37 years old. The third quarter of the ages is the interval 37 to 52, meaning that approximately 25% of the population is between 37 and 52 years old. The fourth quarter of the data is the interval 52 to 99, meaning that approximately 25% of the population is between 52 and 99 years old. The box itself spans the middle 50 percent of the data.
Student A:	I assume that the median age is equal to the median value summarized in the data and that we also summarized in the tables.
Teacher:	Right…, and the median age represents what again?
Student B:	The age in the middle. I recall that to determine the median of a set of data, you would line up the data from smallest to largest and then pick the middle one in that lineup.
Teacher:	On the basis of what you just indicated, interpret for us what the median age represents for each country.
Student C:	The age of a person representing the middle of a lineup of the people in box plot 1 would be 17. This means that 50% of the population was 17 or younger in 2000. That must represent Kenya—as the histograms and tables indicated, Kenya has a younger population. The 50% cumulative percentage would be represented in the 15–19 year-olds.
Student A:	There really is not that much difference in box plots 2 and 3. Box plot 2 has the upper 25% of its population in the range from 57 to 99 years old, while box plot 3 has the upper 25% of its population in the range from 52 to 99 years old.
Student B:	Overall, I think box plot 2 represents a country where a greater percentage of the people are older. Twenty-five percent of the people are squeezed into the range from 57 to 99 years old. I think box plot 2 represents Japan. We noticed earlier that Japan has a greater percentage of older people.
Student C:	We could go back to the table or histogram and add up the percentages of the bars of the histogram and determine in which bar the median age or the approximate age for 50% of the population would be reached. For Japan, that occurs in the 40 to 44 year-old category, and that shows that the median age is in between 40 to 44 years old. Again, box plot 2 would match that value.
Student A:	The box plots—especially the one for Kenya—provide a really neat way to see the spread of the population. I think it is actually the most visually powerful in representing the data.

Teacher: Your point is excellent, especially if we put it all together [*see table 1.5*].

Table 1.5
Quartile Age Ranges for the Three Countries: Kenya, Japan, and the United States

Country	1st quarter age range (first 25% of the population)	2nd quarter age range (next 25% of the population, or 25% to 50% of the cumulative percent)	3rd quarter age range (next 25% of the population, or 50% to 75% of the cumulative percent)	4th quarter age range (last 25% of the population, or 75% to 100% of the cumulative percent)
Kenya	0–7	7–17	17–31	31–99
Japan	0–22	22–42	42–57	57–99
United States	0–17	17–37	37–52	52–99

Discussion with teachers about box plots

The summary from the box plots (see table 1.5) highlights another difference of the distributions, specifically the spread of the ages around the median. The differences in the ages represented by the end of the third quarter range and the end of the first quarter range highlights another important difference between Kenya and the United States or Japan. This difference (also defined as the *interquartile range*, or IQR) is 24 years (or the difference between 31 years and 7 years) for Kenya; the IQR for either the United States or Japan is 35 years.

The greater spread of the ages around the median age for the United States or Japan is best illustrated by examining the box plots. The box plot illustrates a "tighter" fit around the median age for Kenya. This tighter fit, however, also explains why Kenya's histogram has a very different look from the histograms of Japan or the United States.

Why would this difference be important? Here again, allow the students to note the differences in the box plots and histograms and then formulate questions that are linked to the implications for each country as a result of different population distributions. Students might restate and elaborate on their earlier explanations that the special challenges that Kenya faces could be linked to a younger population and the health, economic, or population-density conditions that might result from this different distribution.

Conclusions and Next Steps: Where to Go from Here

The tables provide students with a means to estimate the median age—the middle value of the populations. Students may also be interested in finding the mean age, although the mean age is not necessarily the point that divides the population in half. Making an estimate of the mean age is also not as straightforward, since ages are grouped in 5-year intervals in the data. A relatively quick method that students could use to estimate the mean age for each country is to visually identify the age interval along the age axis that they think would "balance" the distribution as represented by the histogram. (To do this, they would place a pencil or pointer at the position of 0 on the age axis of the histogram. Then they would move the pencil or pointer gradually to the right until they reached a position at which they think the pointer would balance the histogram. The position identified is an estimate of the mean age.)

Comparing the estimates of the median and mean ages of Kenya, Japan, and the United States gives students an insight into the shapes of the population distributions.. The balance point, or mean age, of the population of the United States or Japan does not appear to be noticeably different from the estimate of their median age. If students actually researched the median and mean ages from the United States Census Bureau or the United Nations Web site, they would find that the mean and median ages are not exactly the same for these two countries but are relatively close. A more dramatic difference emerges in the observation that the balance point for Kenya is further to the right than the estimate of the median age. Why is this point to the right of the median? As students move their pencils or pointers to take account of the shorter bars that represent the older population of Kenya, they are estimating that the mean age is greater than the estimate of the median age.

Why is this significant? Students should comment that the population distribution for Kenya looks very different from the population distributions for Japan and the United States and that the differences in these measures of center are one way to highlight the differences. These features provide an explanation of why one histogram looks different from another. (A search of the Web site of the U.S. Census Bureau or the data sites provided by the United Nations previously mentioned would indicate that the difference of the mean and median ages of Kenya is one of the greatest of all countries of the world.)

An Extension of the Population Comparison Task: Changes over Time

Considering how populations change over time is one way of extending students' work with the population comparison task.

Overview for teachers and students

Another representation of each country's population is a population pyramid graph obtained from the United States Census Bureau. A pyramid adds an additional description to the population— namely, a breakdown of the male and female counts for each interval. The pyramid graphs also provide a way to compare the changes in the population over time. Figure 1.6 presents pyramid graphs for 2000 and 2005 for the three countries studied in the investigation.

Extension task for students

Use the pyramid graphs in figure 1.6 to describe how the population of each country has changed from 2000 to 2005 and how you think each country will change in 2010.

Examples of student reasoning and sense making

The following dialogue provides some glimpses of students in the process of reasoning with their teacher as they work with the population pyramid graphs.

Teacher:	What additional information does a population pyramid graph contain?
Student C:	The graphs are similar to the histograms placed on their side.
Student B:	The pyramid graphs are really two histograms—one for males, and one for females.
Teacher:	Why do you think that a breakdown by gender is added to a population pyramid graph?
Student A:	Just like our descriptions of ages earlier, adding the gender provides some indication of the differences in the population.

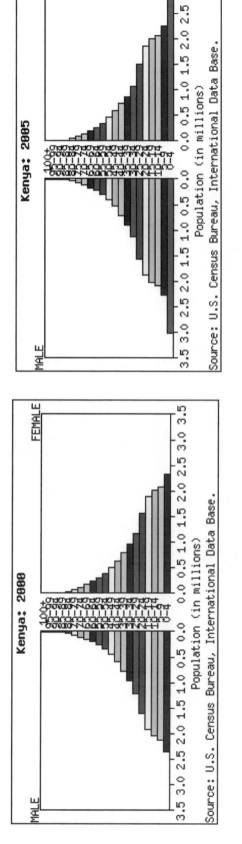

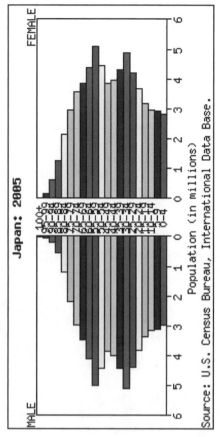

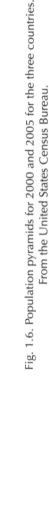

Fig. 1.6. Population pyramids for 2000 and 2005 for the three countries.
From the United States Census Bureau.

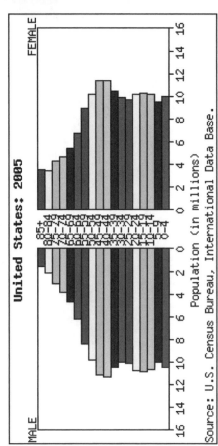

United States: 2000

Population (in millions)

Source: U.S. Census Bureau, International Data Base.

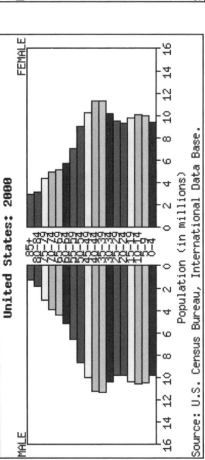

United States: 2005

Population (in millions)

Source: U.S. Census Bureau, International Data Base.

Fig. 1.6—*Continued*

Student B: I think it primarily indicates how the population in the future may change. After all, the percentage of females in a certain age range will help us estimate the number of the new children added to a country.

Teacher: Exactly. And the number of births is used to calculate an important factor—namely, a country's birthrate. Differences in the birthrates of each country are used to estimate how many new people might be added in the future counts of a country's population.

Student A: The Kenya graphs for 2000 and 2005 are very similar. They both indicate that most of the population is young—the four longest layers are 20 and younger in both graphs. Adding the male and female layers is necessary to estimate the median age of the entire country. With these graphs, we can also estimate the median ages for just males or just females.

Student B: The 2005 population has longer bars for 0 to 4 years old for both males and females. It also appears that the entire graph for 2005 looks a little bigger. I think that means Kenya had more children in 2005 as well as a larger total population than in 2000. The number of males to the number of females appears to be very similar for each age category—although there are slightly more males in the 0- to 4-year-olds in 2005.

Teacher: So, how do you think the population of Kenya will look by 2010?

Student A: I think Kenya is growing in total population, since this country will continue to have more children.

Teacher: Would you make the same prediction for Japan?

Student B: Japan's graphs look very similar from 2000 to 2005. I don't think anything changed.

Student A: The 2005 population shows how the population is aging, however. Look at the two longest bars in 2000. The 25- to 29-year-old interval and the 50- to 54-year-old interval are the longest bars in 2000. The longest bars in 2005 are 30- to 34-year-olds and the 55- to 59- year-olds in 2005. This makes perfect sense—people aged by 5 years in all the age categories.

Teacher: How do you think this changes the median age?

Student B: It looks like Japan's population is getting old—the general appearance of the two graphs is the same with most bars moving up. I guess this shows people are aging. I think this suggests the median age will indicate that the population is getting older.

Teacher: How do you think the population of Japan will change in 2010?

Student A: I think people in Japan will continue to get older—that the two longest bars will be represented in the age intervals 35- to 39-year-olds and 60- to 64-year-olds. The 0- to 4-year-olds slightly decreased in 2005 when compared to 2000. I think that the number of 0- to 4-year-olds will also decrease in 2010. Japan's population will be getting older and smaller.

Teacher: And finally, how is the population of the United States changing, and how do you think it will change by 2010?

Student B: The longest bar in 2000 represents the 35- to 39-year-olds. The longest bar in 2005 is 40- to 44-year-olds. I guess that the longest bar in 2010 will be 45 to 49 years old. But, unlike Japan, the youngest age interval (0- to 4-year-olds) increased from 2000 to 2005. If that continues, then the overall population looks like it will be increasing.

Teacher: What do you think is happening to the median age from 2000 to 2010?

Student A: The largest intervals are moving up, suggesting that the median age would be getting older. However, the small increase in the youngest interval (0- to 4-year-olds) suggests that the median age is getting younger. I don't know, but I think the two may cancel each other out—I think the median age from 2000 to 2010 will not change.

Teacher: And how could we estimate the median ages for 2000 and 2005?

Student B: We could simply estimate the values at each age interval and determine the percents.

Note to Teachers

Students can follow up these estimates by creating a table of the values represented in each of the bars. They can organize the data in a format that can be more easily converted to percents. Then they can develop various summaries of the data from that table.

Final Thoughts and Future Directions

Observe that in this investigation the students have used the varying representations of population data from tables, histograms, and box plots to organize their thinking and sense making. These representations highlight the differences and similarities among the age distributions of the populations of the three countries in different ways. The students have calculated and noted various percentages from the tables to compare key demographic groups by ages (e.g., young people, older people); furthermore, they have noted the median age from the box plots to examine the spread of the population from the median age; and finally, they have used the histograms to summarize the rather dramatic different population of Kenya, characterized by the prominence of the younger age ranges, as compared to the older age ranges that are prominent in the population of Japan or the United States.

The students have formed a summary of the population of each country that probably provides them with some answers to the questions raised in the introduction. Now that they have a general summary of each country's population, the follow-up questions that they might ask about each country can move them to the next level in understanding a statistical study. Questions about each country have emerged as a result of their understanding of the country's population. Students might begin to wonder how a country like Kenya provides for the care of a high percentage of young people, or how a country like Japan supports the needs of a higher percentage of older people. Students might wonder if other data (such as income levels or life expectancy or energy consumption) are connected with the different population distributions. These questions—and many others—are likely to be generated by their recognition of how the population distributions differ.

The challenge of collecting or examining data to answer the next set of questions, however, is addressed through the investigations described in the next tasks of this book. Several questions that students might form would need to be addressed by looking at a randomly collected sample of people from each country. How can we collect a meaningful sample? How do we decide if the sample is a good one? Can we generalize the responses from the sample to the larger population?

The country data investigation does not address these questions. The purpose of this investigation is to provide students opportunities to make sense of population data. As students understand a population, however, they begin to formulate more questions that require a more genuine statistical study of data. Often, an initial step of making sense of data is to understand how the collected data are connected with a population. Where did the data come from? How were they collected? How are they represented? Do the data accurately represent the population? What conclusions can be drawn from the process of collecting and representing data?

A reflective look back for teachers

As you focus on reasoning and sense making with your students, you may find it helpful to jot down your observations and reflections in a journal. These can include questions that you have about your students' reasoning as well as thoughts on what you might do differently the next time that you use the investigation with students to push them in their reasoning. In particular, for the population activity, you might consider recording your ideas in response to the following questions:

1. How did students start summarizing the data when it was presented only in the tables?

2. How did the students' conversations change when they were presented with the histograms?

3. How did the students' conversations change when they were presented with the box plots?

4. Describe any connections that students made among key elements of the data (for example, median age, spread, shape of the distributions) across representations.

5. How did the students' reasoning change from their initial responses to the opening questions to the types of reasoning that they were doing later in the investigation? Did the statistical level of their questions evolve as a result of examining the representations in a progression from tables to histograms to box plots?

6. What new questions about data and data representations do you conjecture that students might ask as a result of doing this investigation?

Chapter 2

Eruptions of the Old Faithful Geyser—
Becoming a Data Detective

In this chapter's investigation, students encounter samples of measurement data that occurred in sequence over time. The students construct their own visual displays of the data and then make some estimates and projections based on the data. The importance of attending to variability in the data and the need to track variation in samples of the data over time are major themes in the tasks in this chapter.

The Context

Reasoning and sense making in this investigation involve data on wait times between successive eruptions of geysers. The National Park Service and the U.S. Geological Survey first collected the data in Yellowstone National Park to establish baseline information that could then be used to track and compare long-term behavior of geysers to see whether eruption patterns change or are stable over time. Our investigation focuses on the distribution of wait times between successive eruptions of the Old Faithful geyser (e.g., Hand et al. 1994). It then also examines a second, more recent data set for the geyser (http://geyserstudy.org/OldFaithful_data.htm).

Working with the Old Faithful data set can highlight issues for students about patterns of variability in data and raise questions about potential sources of variation in the data. In addition to reasoning about variability, this exploration prompts students to engage in discourse and reasoning about the variety of possible graphical representations of the distribution of the Old Faithful data and the sensitivity of conclusions from those representations. The data are observational and can be thought of as ordinal data sequenced over time, where the measurement is the wait time between the nth and the $(n + 1)$th eruption of Old Faithful ($n = 1, 2, 3, \ldots$). In this way, students can investigate the distribution of Old Faithful eruption wait times over a set of consecutive observations.

Type of Investigation and Habits of Mind

This investigation is primarily an adventure in exploratory data analysis rather than a statistical experiment. It provides students with an opportunity to be "data detectives," looking for patterns in the variability in the data by comparing different representations of the data. Many statistical reasoning habits surface in this exploration, including (1) attending to and accounting for variability both within and between distributions, (2) reflecting on and conjecturing about the context of the data, and

(3) observing the importance of tracking trends in data over time. Comparisons among representations of data can highlight what is salient or what is hidden in those various representations. Table 2.1 identifies the key element and summarizes the general reasoning habits and the specific statistical reasoning habits of mind that working with this exploration of the Old Faithful data promotes in students.

Table 2.1
Key Element and Habits of Mind in the Old Faithful Data Exploration

---

Key Element: Analyzing Data

Habits of Mind

Analyzing a problem

Looking for patterns and relationships by—
- describing overall patterns in data;
- analyzing and explaining variation;
- making preliminary deductions and conjectures;
- looking for hidden structure in the data.

Implementing a strategy

Selecting representations or procedures by—
- creating meaningful graphical representations and numerical summaries;
- drawing conclusions beyond the data.

Monitoring one's progress

Evaluating a chosen strategy by—
- comparing various graphical and numerical representations;
- comparing various interpretations of the data;
- evaluating the consistency of an observation with a model.

Seeking and using connections

Connecting different representations by—
- noticing connections in a variety of graphical representations;
- connecting conclusions and interpretations to the context.

Reflecting on one's solutions

Checking the reasonableness of an answer by—
- understanding the allowable scope of conclusions;
- determining whether a conclusion based on the data is plausible;
- looking for connections between the data and the context.

The Big Statistical Ideas

The main statistical ideas in this Old Faithful data exploration involve the usefulness of aspects of the distribution of the data—such as shape, center, and spread—in uncovering the inter-eruption behavior of the geyser over time. The activity is designed for small-group exploration with many opportunities to share reasoning—in private-think time, small-group discussions, and whole-class discussion. Although there are times when prompts or questions from the teacher might help focus the discussion and push students to offer justifications, this activity is purposely not heavily scripted. The main idea is to elicit students' thinking and reasoning without too much steering by a teacher. The investigation is designed for students who do have some experience with various ways of representing or graphing data, such as tables, dot plots, box plots, stem-and-leaf plots, and so on.

In the Classroom

In small groups, students create several graphical representations (poster paper recommended) of small samples of the Old Faithful wait-time data. On the basis of the data, they make conjectures about the "expected wait time" for Old Faithful to erupt. Students then justify their reasoning and their decisions while sharing their graphs and conclusions with other groups in whole-class discussion.

A preliminary note to teachers

One delightful thing about this collection of data is that it calls attention to the role that variability plays in reasoning about the data. Observing the up-down swings in the wait times for Old Faithful to erupt, conjecturing what might explain those swings, and noting that mere averages alone can hide the variability in the data are among the central statistical thinking goals in this investigation.

A data analysis exploration like Old Faithful puts the students in the role of "data detectives." In this role, they can compare and contrast various ways of representing the distribution of data. Shape, center, and variability in the data all play roles in the distribution of the data. However, for a data detective, often the "story" in the data lies in the variability in them—how the data are distributed across the range of observations. The process of asking students to make lists of "notices" and "wonders" is one way to help catalyze the process of critical thinking. "Notices" are observations that are fairly evident from the data or the claims made by a statistical study. However, "notices" can also lead to questions: "I notice *that*…, and that made me *wonder* about…."

To reflect the variety of backgrounds and experiences that students bring to the work of representing data graphically, this investigation presents a wide spectrum of excerpts of students' reasoning. The examples of students' reasoning that we share reflect a range, from reasoning that is quite naïve and unsophisticated to reasoning that is more mature and could even include measurements and some summary statistics. This range illustrates the possibilities in reasoning that we have seen in students when we have conducted this activity with them.

Summary of the task, and the statistical question

Table 2.2 contains consecutive eruption wait times in minutes for the Old Faithful geyser in Yellowstone National Park, collected in 1985. The wait times for the geyser cover consecutive eruptions over a period of about two weeks. Each row in the table represents approximately one day's worth of eruption wait times for Old Faithful.

Table 2.2
Old Faithful Data—Minutes Between Blasts

1)	86	71	57	80	75	77	60	86	77	56	81	50	89	54	90	73	60	83
2)	65	82	84	54	85	58	79	57	88	68	76	78	74	85	75	65	76	58
3)	91	50	87	48	93	54	86	53	78	52	83	60	87	49	80	60	92	43
4)	89	60	84	69	74	71	108	50	77	57	80	61	82	48	81	73	62	79

Table 2.2—*Continued*

5)	54	80	73	81	62	81	71	79	81	74	59	81	66	87	53	80	50	87
6)	51	82	58	81	49	92	50	88	62	93	56	89	51	79	58	82	52	88
7)	52	78	69	75	77	53	80	55	87	53	85	61	93	54	76	80	81	59
8)	86	78	71	77	76	94	75	50	83	82	72	77	75	65	79	72	78	77
9)	79	75	78	64	80	49	88	54	85	51	96	50	80	78	81	72	75	78
10)	87	69	55	83	49	82	57	84	57	84	73	78	57	79	57	90	62	87
11)	78	52	98	48	78	79	65	84	50	83	60	80	50	88	50	84	74	76
12)	65	89	49	88	51	78	85	65	75	77	69	92	68	87	61	81	55	93
13)	53	84	70	73	93	50	87	77	74	72	82	74	80	49	91	53	86	49
14)	79	89	87	76	59	80	89	45	93	72	71	54	79	74	65	78	57	87
15)	72	84	47	84	57	87	68	86	75	73	53	82	93	77	54	96	48	89
16)	63	84	76	62	83	50	85	78	78	81	78	76	74	81	66	84	48	93

Students select several days (rows) of data and make a decision based on their data about how long they would expect to wait for an eruption of Old Faithful. The presentation of the task to students asks them (1) to make one or more graphical representations of their data, (2) to decide as a group how long they would expect to wait for Old Faithful to erupt, and (3) to share their graphs, reasoning, and conjectures with the other groups of students in the class.

The Old Faithful task as presented to students

Teachers can introduce the task to the students as follows:

> This investigation involves data on wait times between successive eruptions (blasts) of geysers that were first collected by the National Park Service and the U.S. Geological Survey in Yellowstone National Park. The data were collected to establish some baseline information that could then be used to track and compare long-term behavior of geysers. Hundreds of thousands of people come to Yellowstone Park every year, and most of them include a visit to the Old Faithful geyser, and the question always arises about how long they will have to wait until Old Faithful erupts again. In this investigation, you will put on a "data detective" hat and investigate some data from Old Faithful to conjecture about the time that someone might expect to wait for Old Faithful to erupt, as well as about some factors that could affect that wait time.
>
> **Directions**: In your group, pick any two rows of these wait times so that your group has two sample days of Old Faithful wait times. (A group member might be asked to pick two numbers between 1 and 16 to pick the two rows, so that every group does not pick the same two rows. Using a random device to pick the rows would be best, if one is available).
>
> *First, working individually, take the following steps:*
>
> 1.   Look over the data. Is there anything that you notice, or anything that you wonder about in your two samples of data? Jot down some "notices" and "wonders."

2.   Create at least one type of graphical representation for each of the two days of data to help you visualize any patterns in the wait times. Jot down any additional notices and wonders that occur to you.

Next, working as a group, do the following:

3.   Share and compare. Share your graphical representations of the data in your group. What do you notice, or wonder about, as you look through your group's graphical representations?

4.   Accept your challenge as data detectives. Agree as a group on a graphical way to display your data. On the basis of your data, make a group decision about how long you would expect to wait between blasts of Old Faithful if you showed up at Yellowstone Park and Old Faithful had just finished erupting. Be prepared to present your graph to the other groups in class and to defend your group's data-based prediction for the expected wait time.

Students' Reasoning and Sense Making about the Data

In our presentation of student reasoning, we suppose that the groups selected rows 2 and 3 in table 2.2:

2)   65 82 84 54 85 58 79 57 88 68 76 78 74 85 75 65 76 58
3)   91 50 87 48 93 54 86 53 78 52 83 60 87 49 80 60 92 43

Graphical representations could be constructed either by hand or by using a technological tool, such as a graphing calculator, a spreadsheet, or a statistics and data software program. The graphs in the following discussion are typical of those that students have created when we have used the Old Faithful data with them.

> ### Note to Teachers
> *Your students might share reasoning patterns that are similar to those in the examples, or they might find a surprising "new way" to represent the data that surfaces. By not over-scripting the discussion, the authors hope to allow students' own reasoning to emerge and to allow you to guide the sequencing of issues in the discussion. This will mean that as students are working in groups, you can circulate and make a plan for sequencing the presentation of their thinking when they share the graphs (posters) of the Old Faithful data, saving some of the more sophisticated reasoning for later presentations.*

Examples of typical student graphs and reasoning

The following examples illustrate students' reasoning in the analysis phase of the investigation.

Groups A–D

Group A: We graphed each wait time for day 2 [*see fig. 2.1*]. Some wait times are high, like over 80 minutes, and some are as low as in the 50s. We picked a time more in the middle for our prediction, as some would be higher, some lower, but there were a lot of middle-height bars that were around 70, so we think we'd have to wait about 70 minutes.

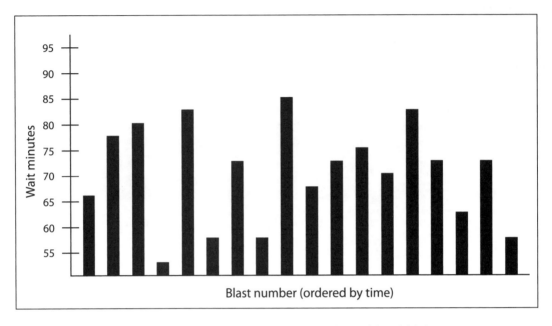

Fig. 2.1. Group A's graphical representation of the Old Faithful data

Group B: We made stem-and-leaf plots for our data for day 3 [*see fig. 2.2*]. We calculated the average wait time to be about 68 minutes, so we would predict we'd wait about that long—about an hour. We noticed that there was a lot of variation in our data—a very wide spread—so we used the average as a middle point.

9	1, 2
8	0, 3, 6, 7, 7
7	8
6	0, 0
5	0, 2, 3, 4
4	3, 8, 9
tens	ones

Fig. 2.2. Group B's stem-and-leaf plot of eruption interval times for Old Faithful

Note to Teachers

If students make a stem-and-leaf plot and calculate the mean as group B did, you might ask them also to find the median, since it is so readily available—60 minutes in this case. Furthermore, you might ask the students what might cause the mean and median to be so different in this case.

Group C: We made frequency graphs, but we seemed to get different shapes depending on our choice of interval widths for the frequencies. For example, on the basis of our first graph [*see fig. 2.3*], we'd expect to wait about 75 minutes, because it shows most wait times for the eruption in the 75- to 79-minute range. This graph had just a few data points down at the lower end, but most everything is up around the 75 to 79 range, and the graph is pretty symmetric around 75, with those few lower exceptions that cluster in the 50s.

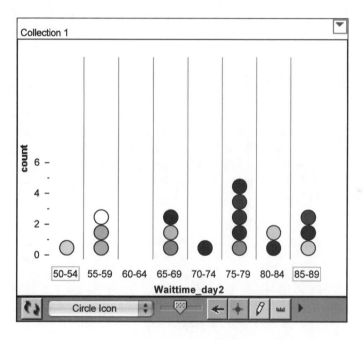

Fig. 2.3. Group C's first graphical representation of the Old Faithful data

But then we saw that if we chose our intervals [*also called* bin widths] in another way [*see fig. 2.4*], we obtained something that looks very different. There is no obvious pattern here, and we thought that a person could just as easily wait about 55, or 75, or 85 minutes, because all three of those times were equally frequent in this graph, each occurring 4 times.

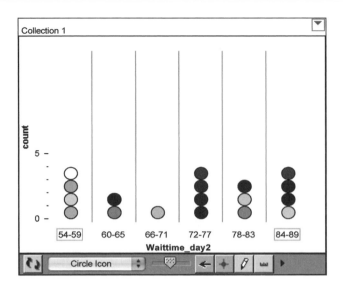

Fig. 2.4. Group C's second graphical representation of the Old Faithful data

Group D: We made a box plot for the day 2 data [*see fig. 2.5*], because the data were kind of spread out, from 50 to 90 minutes. Because the median is 75 minutes in the box plot, we thought 75 minutes would be about how long we'd expect to have to wait for Old Faithful to erupt. But then we made a box plot of the day 3 data [*also in fig. 2.5*], and the median value there is 69 minutes, but 69 minutes never occurred in our data! So then we thought maybe that the data in the box would be a better measure of expected wait times because the data are so spread out. Then we superimposed dot plots [*in fig. 2.5*] under the box plots to show exactly how the data points are distributed across those box plots.

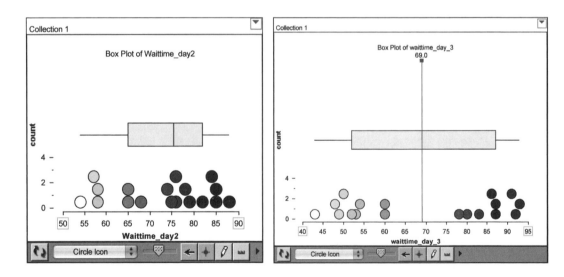

Fig. 2.5. Group D's box plots for day 2 and day 3, combined with dot plot representations of the Old Faithful data

Comparing the middle 50% of the data from day 2 and day 3, the middle 50% goes from 65 minutes to 82 minutes for day 2, and from about 53 minutes to 87 minutes for day 3. So, overall from the two days combined, we concluded that 50% of the time you'd probably have to wait at least an hour, and perhaps as much as an hour and 20 minutes, because that's the middle 50% of the box plots.

Discussion with teachers on the reasoning and graphs of groups A–D. The types of graphs and reasoning shared above by students in groups A–D are typical of what students do and how they think about the data. Most of their decisions on how long to wait for Old Faithful are based on measures of center. Groups A and C reasoned from "mosts" in their prediction criteria, suggesting that either the mode or a modal clump was influencing their predictions. Group B used the mean, and group D at first used the median for its prediction. Then, however, the students in group D began to think about how to account for the range and variation of their data because their second graph did not actually have any data values that were at or very near the median value.

Although it is more likely that students would construct either box plots or dot plots alone, we combined the two graphs—a dot plot superimposed on a box plot—in our presentation of the reasoning of group D because we have seen cross comparisons of graphical displays emerge in the explanations of students who are a bit more mature in their statistical reasoning. If your students produced only comparative box plots for the two days of data, you have an opportunity to ask them questions about how the data are really distributed in those box plots, and how they could show the real distributions. Box plots are great for quick summaries, but they are also notorious for masking aspects of the distribution of data.

Group C obtained two frequency distributions that appear to be quite different. It is common for students to discover that bin-width choices yield seemingly different visual displays of a distribution, since the shape of a frequency distribution can be quite sensitive to the interval-width choice. This is an important issue to bring to students' attention if such examples arise in your class. You then have an opportunity to raise questions about the wisdom of making predictions based purely on the shape of the data. We need to ask students to look for other, more robust ways of representing the data to avoid the distractions of visual shape in the display, since shape alone can mislead someone making predictions. Thus, you can underscore the importance of representing the data in multiple ways before making any conjectures.

The reasoning gradually became more sophisticated in group D's analysis when the students began to try to take variation into account in their prediction. The usefulness of taking account of variation is a very important idea to highlight. Center values alone (mean, median, mode) can mask what is really going on in a data set like that for the eruptions of Old Faithful. Because the Old Faithful data distribution is not mound shaped—e.g., it is not *unimodal*—a central value can hide the real story in the variability in these data.

In fact, as we will see when we accumulate the data for many days, the data appear to form two clusters, which are beginning to emerge even in group D's graphs for only one day. Note that if group D presented just the box plots alone, they would mask the *bimodal* shape of the data set. You might ask students to make comparisons across the set of graphs that they have constructed. Can they find connections among them? Do trends in one type of graph (center, spread, shape) show up somewhere in another graphical representation? Can consistent conjectures about Old Faithful's wait time be made from their set of graphs, or do conflicting conjectures arise, depending on how the data are represented? Consider the reasoning of the students in group E. Their thinking represents another trajectory.

Group E

Group E: We made graphs somewhat like group A's graph, but we plotted the wait time for each blast in succession for day 3 [*see fig. 2.6*]. We think we see a pattern in the data. There seems to be an up-down pattern in the wait times in day 3. It was easier to see when we connected the dots in our plot. Then we did the same thing for day 2, and the up-down pattern in wait times appears there, too. It's not always perfect, but a long wait time is usually followed by a short time, and a short one by a long one.

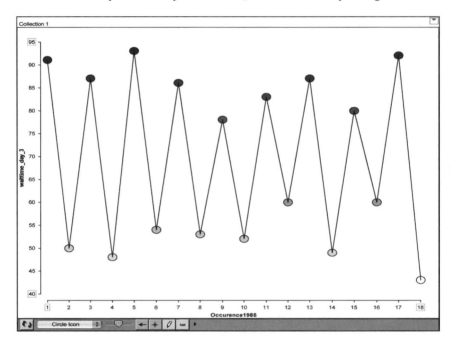

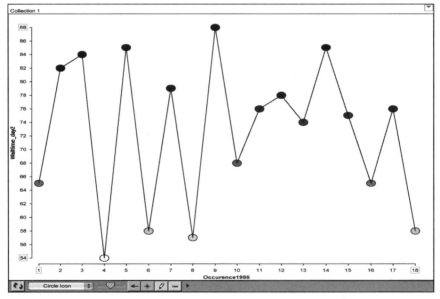

Fig. 2.6. Group E's plots over time of the Old Faithful data

Discussion with teachers on the reasoning and graphs of group E. We have often found that at least one group of students will construct a graph that uncovers the pattern that group E discovered. (If this doesn't occur when you try the investigation, you might prompt this observation by asking your students to compare successive blasts.) Once students notice the pattern, they can raise other questions and conjectures, such as the following:

- Why are these alternating wait times happening?
- Do all geysers behave this way, or is it just Old Faithful?
- Would similar behavior show up in other years for Old Faithful, or did this happen just in 1985?
- What is Old Faithful doing this year? Has the geyser persisted in the up-down behavior for the wait times, or have things changed since 1985?

A statistical investigation that involves data analysis often elicits further statistical questions, and for this reason, data analysis and statistics can provide a very rich environment for student reasoning and sense making.

Further reasoning and sense making catalyzed by group E's discovery

Consider the reasoning of three students about the alternating short and long wait times discerned by group E:

Student G: Why would the pattern be short-long alternating for wait times? Do you suppose it has something to do with how long Old Faithful blows—like, if it erupts for a long time, maybe there is a long wait time for the next eruption?

Student H: There must be some geothermal pressure pools forming to account for this short-long pattern. If we knew what the previous wait time was, we could predict the length of the next wait time more accurately, depending on whether the previous one was long or short.

Student I: If we plot *all* the wait times that we have for Old Faithful on one graph [*see fig. 2.7*], we can see two distinct "clumps" of data, one representing the short wait times, and the other the long wait times. One clump goes from about 48 to 58 minutes, and the other clump from about 65 to 85 minutes.

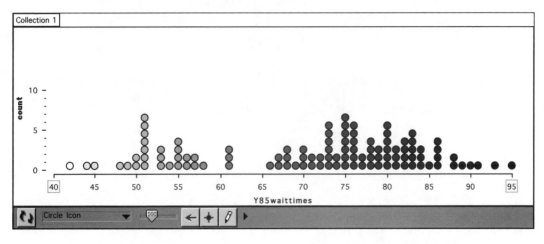

Fig. 2.7. A dot plot of all the wait times for the 1985 data collected for Old Faithful

Conclusion and Next Steps: Where to Go from Here

The Old Faithful data for this period of time in 1985 clearly form a bimodal distribution, alternating between shorter and longer wait times, for the most part. Student H even conjectured that if we knew the previous wait time, we could predict the next wait time more accurately. Questions also are likely to arise about whether this type of behavior in the eruption wait times persists over time, maintaining the shorter-longer pattern, or whether it changes. The extension tasks below provide opportunities for teachers and students to push their reasoning and sense making further by following up on some of the questions and observations that the students may have made during their initial investigation.

Extension task 1

Figure 2.8 is a scatter plot of Old Faithful wait time plotted against the immediately previous wait time. Show this graph to the students and ask them what they notice ("notices"), and what they wonder about ("wonders"). The reference lines (horizontal and vertical) are the median wait time for each set of blasts.

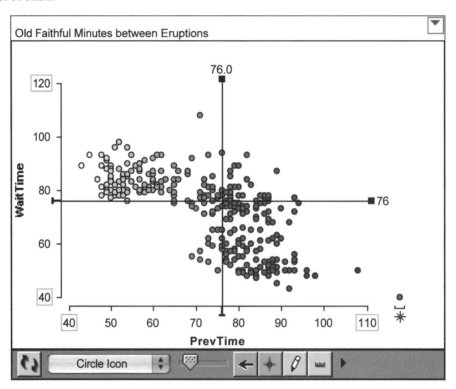

Fig. 2.8. A scatter plot of Old Faithful wait time vs. previous wait time

Note to Teachers

In inspecting a scatter plot like that in figure 2.8, students may notice that the second and fourth "quadrants" created by the median cross hairs are very full of data, whereas the first and third quadrants are relatively devoid of data. Ask students what this means. You may need to prompt them if they do not remark on this situation in their "notices" and "wonders." Make sure that your students understand what this graph is telling them. For example, can they find the short wait times followed by long wait times, or the long wait times followed by short wait times, in the graph? Where do these show up in it?

Extension task 2

Figure 2.9 shows a dot plot of the entire two weeks of data on wait times for eruptions of Old Faithful from 1985. Students might extend their reasoning and sense making by considering the following three questions:

1. Compare the data in your own two chosen sample days with the data from the entire data set. Do your two days appear to be *representative* of the entire data set? Explain.

2. Would you change your conclusion about your expected wait time on the basis of the entire two weeks' wait times? Why, or why not?

3. Are there other data about Old Faithful that you think might provide important information for making a prediction for wait time?

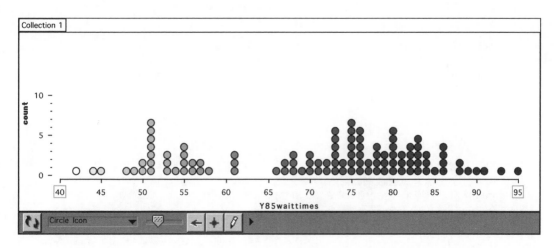

Fig. 2.9. A dot plot of all the wait times for the 1985 data collected for Old Faithful

Note to Teachers

Some days' data on Old Faithful exhibit the overall bimodal picture clearly; other days' data show it less clearly. Thus, students' answers to the question, "Do your two days appear to be 'representative' of the entire data set?" will depend on their particular days. Some students might not have noticed the bimodal, or short-long, pattern in wait times when they did their own analysis and graphical representations of the data. Once they have analyzed the entire data set, they might indeed make a new prediction in response to the question, "Would you change your conclusion about your expected wait time on the basis of the entire two weeks' wait times?". Many might advocate reporting two "centers." You might nudge them a bit, helping them see that the answer to how long they have to wait is, in fact, "It depends." What other data might students find useful? We have found that some students would really like to know the duration time of Old Faithful's blasts, since they conjecture that long blast times might be followed by longer wait times, and short blasts by short wait times until the next eruption. Other students might want to learn about time of day or temperature and other meteorological variables during the blasts.

Extension task 3

Consider the following question: What if we compared wait times between eruptions of Old Faithful across several years—has the pattern in the 1985 data continued, or has it changed? Figure 2.10 contains dot plots for the same two weeks' worth of consecutive eruption wait times for the years 1985 and 2003. Pose the following two questions to your students:

1. What do you notice in these graphs? What do you wonder about?

2. How would you describe the 2003 Old Faithful wait times, compared to the 1985 Old Faithful wait times, with respect to shape, center, and spread?

Note to Teachers

Students should notice that the data for 2003 show no apparent bimodal shape in distribution, suggesting that perhaps the short-long pattern that was evident in 1985 may have disappeared by 2003. Perhaps there is some geothermal or geological explanation (e.g., was there an earthquake in between these years?) for this apparent change—a speculation that presents an opportunity to press for more information from the Park Service in Yellowstone. In any event, the center of the distribution appears to be higher in the data for 2003, meaning that the average wait time was longer in 2003.

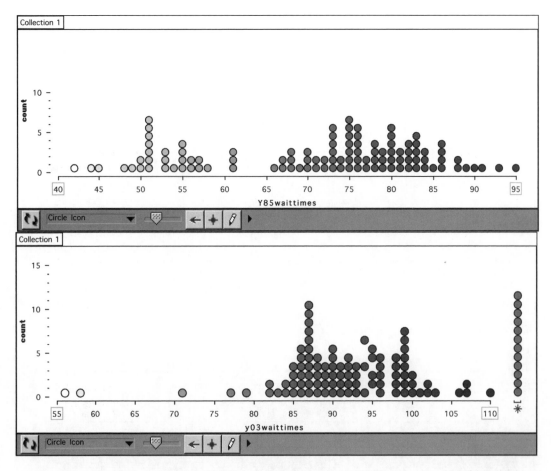

Fig. 2.10. A dot plot comparison of 1985 wait time data with 2003 wait time data for Old Faithful

The data for 2003 show a clustering into one clump, as opposed to the two clumps evident in 1985. Visual inspection thus suggests that the 2003 data are unimodal and more tightly packed than the data for 1985, and the more recent data reflect a higher average wait time. Students' observations of these facts provide an opportunity for some more specific statistical follow-up questions such as the following:

1. Find a measure of center and spread for each of these two distributions of data, 1985 and 2003 (e.g., means and standard deviations).

2. On the basis of these measures and your graphs, what can you conclude about the distribution of wait times in 2003, when compared to the distribution of wait times in 1985?

Note to Teachers

Depending on the experience of your students, they could calculate their own means and standard deviations for the two distributions, or they could find medians and create 50% box plots. Alternatively, you could provide them with a copy of figure 2.11, in which the vertical reference lines on the fulcrum triangles indicate the means (balance points) of each distribution, and the box length on either side of the mean is the standard deviation of each distribution.

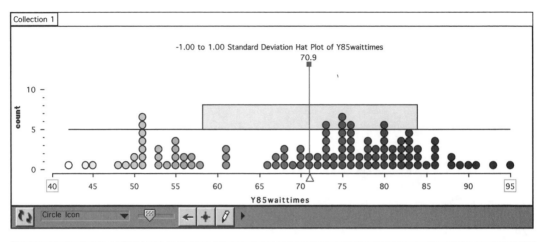

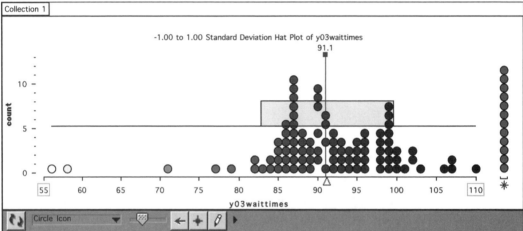

Fig. 2.11. Graphical displays of the means and standard deviation box for the 1985 and 2003 Old Faithful data

As indicated in figure 2.11, the mean wait time for 1985 is approximately 71 minutes, and the standard deviation (SD) from the mean is approximately 12 minutes (71 ± 12 minutes, in the 1985 SD box). Similarly, for 2003, the mean wait time is approximately 91 minutes, and the standard deviation is approximately 9 minutes.

Final Thoughts

One of the big ideas that the Old Faithful data set can help students develop is that there is more to life—and statistical analysis—than centers (mean, median, mode). We need to consider a number of attributes when analyzing a distribution of data, including shape and dispersion as well as center. Measures of center provide valuable summaries for data, but they can also hide patterns in the variation in the data and mask interesting behavior in the data if we rely on them alone.

When we observe a pattern in the variation of the data, as in this case, we need to seek an explanation for that pattern. Perhaps in the case of Old Faithful there are geothermal explanations—for example, perhaps the length of the actual blast time is an important variable to research in determining the wait time until the next blast. To answer such questions, we would need additional data. When students generate questions that relate the data to its context, when they ask questions that suggest the need for further explorations and extensions, they are indicating that they themselves are taking ownership of the reasoning and sense making in the problem. We then need to provide them with opportunities—and time—to pursue their own questions, since their own questions are what motivate deeper reasoning and sense making.

A reflective look back for teachers

As you focus on reasoning and sense making with your students, you may find it helpful to jot down your observations and reflections in a journal. These can include questions that you have about your students' reasoning as well as thoughts on what you might do differently the next time you use the investigation with students to push them in their reasoning. In particular, for the Old Faithful activity, you might consider recording your ideas in response to the following questions:

1. What did you learn about your students' reasoning about data in the Old Faithful activity? Did things happen that you expected? Was there anything that surprised you?

2. Where in your curriculum, or your school setting, do your students already have, or could you create, an opportunity for them to reason about data as students did in the Old Faithful activity?

3. How might you do things differently if you were to provide your students with an opportunity to redo any of the Old Faithful tasks?

Shaughnessy and Pfannkuch (2002) offer more discussion about the nature of statistical thinking and the Old Faithful activity.

Chapter 3

Will Women Run Faster
than Men in the Olympics?

The question posed in the title of this chapter cannot be answered for certain. However, students can develop a plausible answer to it by reasoning with data and applying important connections to other aspects of their growing awareness of mathematics.

The Context

This investigation presents students with available Olympic data and asks them to develop a statistical model that can help answer the question. The data were collected at each of the modern Olympics that included the 200-meter dash. Students think about how this observed data could be analyzed. They are often amazed by the patterns that emerge and the implications. The dialogue in this chapter is intended to demonstrate some typical student reasoning and sense making about comparing data sets collected over time.

The Big Statistical Ideas

The discussions in this chapter focus on interpreting and developing various equations of least-squares regression lines. It is important that students think and reason about regression lines as summary representations of data that can be used to make conjectures about the data. Although understanding all the aspects of the specific techniques is not critical for deriving the equation of the regression line, students should examine the line's fit to a scatter plot of the data, describe how the data are distributed in the plane about a line of fit, and draw appropriate conclusions to address questions posed about the data, such as the Olympic comparison question posed for the investigation. In the end, students may conclude that the question cannot be answered with the data at hand, but the process of reaching that conclusion is important in developing their reasoning and sense making skills. Table 3.1 identifies the key element and summarizes the general reasoning habits and the specific statistical reasoning habits of mind that are involved in this investigation.

Table 3.1
Key Element and Habits of Mind in the Olympic Exploration

Key Element: Analyzing Data

Habits of Mind

Analyzing a problem

Looking for patterns and relationships by—
- describing overall patterns in data;
- looking for hidden structure in the data;
- making preliminary deductions and conjectures.

Monitoring one's progress

Evaluating a chosen strategy by—
- evaluating the consistency of an observation with a model;
- applying the iterative statistical process to the investigation.

Seeking and using connections

Connecting different representations by—
- identifying common components of analyses (e.g., standardization);
- understanding the sensitivity of an analysis to various components;
- connecting conclusions and interpretations to the context.

Reflecting on one's solutions

Checking the reasonableness of an answer by—
- determining whether a conclusion based on the data is plausible;
- justifying or validating the solution or conclusion.

Introduction to the Task

The Summer Olympic games are generally held every four years. They provide an opportunity for athletes from all over the world to compete. As expected, this level of competition results in the best athletes demonstrating their abilities to run, jump, throw, wrestle, box, and excel in many other individual and team sports. The track and field events are particularly noteworthy, as the Olympics provide a prime-time audience with access to competitions not normally showcased. The running events are frequently won or lost by a fraction of a second. The gold medal times for the 200-meter dash are listed in table 3.2 and represent all of the modern-day Olympic winning times from 1900 to 2004 for this race.

This investigation calls on students to examine the data in the table and consider the following question: Can you use these data to predict the future times of men and women in this event? Do you think women will ever run faster than men, and if yes, when? Construct an argument to support your answer to this question by using data.

Table 3.2
Times for the Olympic 200-Meter Dash

Year	Male	Time (in seconds)	Female	Time (in seconds)
1900	Walter Tewksbury, USA	22.2		
1904	Archie Hahn, USA	21.6		
1908	Robert Kerr, Canada	22.6		
1912	Ralph Craig, USA	21.7		
1920	Allan Woodring, USA	22.0		
1924	Jackson Scholz, USA	21.6		
1928	Percy Williams, Canada	21.8		
1932	Eddie Tolan, USA	21.12		
1936	Jesse Owens, USA	20.70		
1948	Mel Patton, USA	21.10	Fanny Blankers-Koen, NED	24.40
1952	Andy Stanfield, USA	20.81	Marjorie Jackson, AUS	23.89
1956	Bobby Morrow, USA	20.75	Betty Cuthbert, AUS	23.55
1960	Livio Berruti, ITA	20.62	Wilma Rudolph, USA	24.13
1964	Henry Carr, USA	20.36	Edith McGuire, USA	23.05
1968	Tommie Smith, USA	19.83	Irena Szewinska, Poland	22.58
1972	Valeriy Borzov, USSR	20.00	Renate Stecher, GDR	22.40
1976	Don Quarrie, JAM	20.23	Barbel Eckert, GDR	22.37
1980	Pietro Mennea, ITA	20.19	Barbel Wockel (Eckert), GDR	22.03
1984	Carl Lewis, USA	19.80	Valerie Brisco-Hooks, USA	21.81
1988	Joe DeLoach, USA	19.75	Florence Griffith-Joyner, USA	21.34
1992	Mike Marsh, USA	20.01	Gwen Torrence, USA	21.81
1996	Michael Johnson, USA	19.32	Marie-Jose Perec, FRA	22.12
2000	Konstantinos Kenteris, GRE	20.09	Marion Jones, USA	21.84
2004	Shawn Crawford, USA	19.79	Veronica Campbell, JAM	22.05

Note to Teachers

Discussion suggestions on the table. *Data are initially presented in this investigation in a table. Students should be directed to reflect on the data, how they were collected, and how they might be used to develop a conjecture related to the initial question of the investigation. To make sense of data, students need to be challenged to explain what bivariate data represent and to portray the "story behind the numbers" in this context. The data set provides an opportunity for students to expand their understanding of the organization of data and leads to the development of mathematical equations to estimate future times. The 2008 Olympic times are not included in this table, but they are used at the conclusion of this investigation to examine students' reasoning as they apply the models that they have built.*

As you start the investigation, give students time to reflect individually on how the table is organized and what information is summarized. Then organize the students in small groups to share their thoughts about the information and how they might use it to address the initial question. Finally, groups could share their ideas in a whole-class discussion.

Students' Reasoning about the Table

The following dialogue reflects the reasoning of actual students.

Teacher: The data for the Olympic event are recorded in seconds. Before we discuss the task, explain what data are summarized in this table.

Student 1:   The data include the year in which the Olympics was held, the name of the person and country who received the gold medal, and the time for that event.

Teacher: Are there any questions that you have about the data presented in this table?

Student 2:   I am interested why were there so many years with only men's times.

Teacher: Women's events were not held in the 200-meter event until 1948. You will also notice that there were years that the Olympics were not held at all. If the 4-year pattern had been followed, there should have been an Olympics in 1916, 1940, and 1944. These games were canceled because of World War I and World War II. The incredible performance of Jesse Owens at the 1936 Olympics is often highlighted as a major event that is connected to World War II—you will notice that he got the gold medal in this event in the last Olympics held before World War II…. In your groups, discuss the question, "Will women ever run faster than men in this race?" How do you suggest that we examine the data represented in the table to answer the question?

Student 1:   I think it is actually rather obvious – the women's time for any Olympic year was always slower than the men's time.

Teacher: Yes, but are there any interesting ways in which the relationship is changing?

Student 2:   In 1948, the difference in the women's time versus the men's time was 3.3 seconds. In 2004, the difference was 2.26 seconds—women seem to be closing the gap.

Student 3:   There are other years, however, where the gap was even larger. Let's calculate this for each of the Olympic years that men and women were involved [*see table 3.3*].

Table 3.3
Gap Times between Men and Women Victors for the Olympic 200-Meter Dash

Year	1948	1952	1956	1960	1964	1968	1972	1976
Difference in times (in seconds)	3.30	3.08	2.80	3.51	2.69	2.75	2.40	2.14

Year	1980	1984	1988	1992	1996	2000	2004
Difference in times (in seconds)	1.84	2.01	1.59	1.80	2.80	1.75	2.26

Student 1:   These gaps bounce around, but over time, it seems that the gap is getting smaller.

Students' Reasoning about the Scatter Plot

Table 3.2 shows *bivariate data* collected in time sequence. The table shows measurement observations for two variables, men's running times and women's running times. Bivariate data often can be represented in a scatter plot in the plane, such as the plot in figure 3.1, and lines, or curvilinear functions, can sometimes "fit" the data points. Software tools typically can fit a *least-squares regression line* or a *median-median line* to bivariate data.

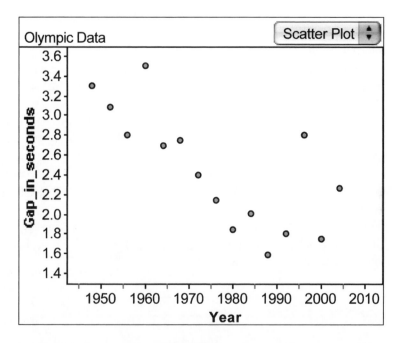

Fig. 3.1. A scatter plot of time differences—gaps—between men's
and women's Olympic 200-meter winning times

As the dialogue with the students continues, the least-squares line is superimposed on a scatter plot of the time "gaps" between the men's and women's times plotted over the Olympic years. Students should notice that the points do not really fit the regression line very well and that the distances from the scattered points to the line of fit vary noticeably.

Note to Teachers

The source of the actual equations of these least-squares regression or median-median lines is not so important for our investigation. For our purposes, it is more important that students analyze and critique whether or not the line does a reasonable job of fitting the scattered points. In many introductory investigations with data, students can "eyeball" a line to help them develop their intuition about the usefulness of lines to make predictions for what will occur in the future, on the basis of current trends in the data.

Teacher: We suggested examining the Olympic gaps with a scatter plot [*see fig. 3.1*]. Why do you think a scatter plot might help us answer our questions?

Student 2:   A scatter plot shows how the year and the times connect. The year of the Olympics is the *x*-value, and the difference between the men's and women's times is the *y*-value.

Student 3:   And I think that by organizing the data this way, we can see how the gaps are changing over the years.

Teacher: How are they changing?

Student 1:   Although it's not a consistent pattern, the big picture when I stand back looks like the gaps are declining over the years. There are a few years in which the gaps were much wider and threw off this pattern. For example, I wonder why the gaps in 1960 and 1996 were so much greater than the other gaps?

Student 2:   Is there a pattern over time that we can use to predict the future?

Teacher: Your question is directly behind what I am asking you to think about. As you mentioned, our *x*-values of the scatter plot are the Olympic years. Can we use the Olympic years to predict the *y*-values, or the gaps?

Student 3:   I am sure we will not be able to predict it exactly, but maybe we could trace the pattern and come up with a pretty good guess. We would be looking for when the gap is 0 seconds.

Teacher: That is an excellent way to proceed. We'll need to summarize the pattern in some mathematical way.… The computer indicates that the *least-squares regression line* for this scatter plot is

"Differences in time" = (–0.0245) * Year + 50.86.

Look at the line [*see fig. 3.2*]. Let's start with the slope. What is the slope of this line, and what does it mean in our context?

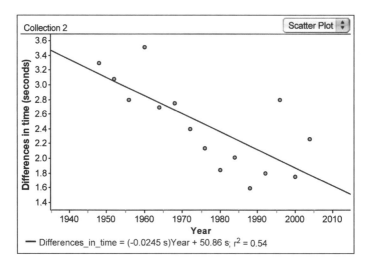

Fig. 3.2. A scatter plot and regression line for differences in men's and women's 200-meter times

Student 1:   Well, since this line is going down, the slope is negative. The equation indicates that the slope is –0.0245. The gap is in seconds, and the time is in years. So, the gap between the men and women is going down on average by a little more than 2 hundredths of a second per year.

Student 2:   But the Olympics are held only once every 4 years.

Student 1:   So if I multiply the slope by 4, I would get an estimate of the change in the gap be-tween Olympics. In that case, the gap looks like it would go down on average by a little more than 8 hundredths of a second. The actual gap times from past Olympics are bouncing around, so I don't know if that is a good indication of what is happening.

Teacher: If the gap were decreasing over time, how could we use it to determine when women would run faster than men?

Student 3:   If the gap were 0, then women and men would have approximately the same times. So, if we set the differences in time value in the equation to 0 and then find the year, that would indicate when the men and women would run the race with the same times, or, in other words,

$$0 = (-0.0245) * \text{Year} + 50.86,$$
$$-50.86 = -0.0245 * \text{Year},$$
$$-50.86 / -0.0245 = \text{Year}.$$

So the year is approximately 2076. This indicates that if the gaps continue to close at the same rate, then in the year 2076—if there is an Olympics in that year—the times should be approximately the same.

Teacher: Do you think the equation for the gap is a good one?

Student 2:   No! The points in the scatter plot look like they are going down, but the points don't seem to match the line very well.

Teacher: Very good observation. Let's look at some specific examples. On the one hand, the equation does a good job of predicting the gap in 1964, since the actual gap is 2.69 seconds, and the predicted gap from the equation is 2.74 seconds. That is a difference of 0.05 seconds. On the other hand, it does not do a good job of predicting the gap in 1996. The actual gap for that year is 2.80 seconds, but the predicted gap based on the equation is 1.96 seconds. That is a difference of 0.84 seconds. That seems like a big difference for this event. I wonder why it's so great?

Note to Teachers

Encourage students to reflect on the human factors that are connected with this type of data. For example, could weather or the environment have influenced the times? Urge students to speculate on what other factors might explain the variations in times from the predicted values.

Comparing Plots of Men's and Women's Winning Times in Olympic Years

The next part of the students' conversation is based on their examination of a scatter plot like that in figure 3.3, which displays the actual times for men and women in the 200-meter dash for each of the Olympic years. The scatter plot provides another opportunity to address the investigation's initial question with different regression lines.

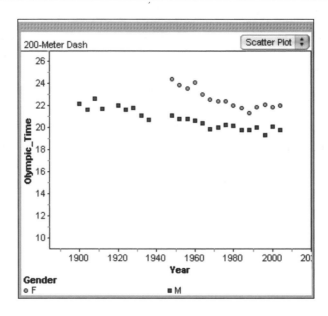

Fig. 3.3. Scatter plots over time of men's and women's 200-meter Olympic times

Teacher: Let's look at the data another way. Let's examine the actual male and female times over time. A scatter plot from our computer [*see fig. 3.3*] provides a different-looking graph of these times and gives us another way to think about our question.

Student 1:   Ah! Now the differences between men and women are clearer. The men's times are going down, and so are the women's times. But the men's times look like they are not going down as steeply.

Student 2:   I agree, but the women's times seem to have gone down steadily until the last four Olympics on the scatter plot. I'm not sure what that means.

Students' Reasoning with Regression Lines

The conversation continues, with a student drawing a regression line on the scatter plot that was shown in figure 3.3:

Student 3:   My calculator will draw and calculate the regression line that fits these points [*see fig. 3.4*]. Let's make one line each for the men's times and the women's times.

Student 2:   The women's times do not seem to be as close to the line, but they clearly look as if they are decreasing more steeply than the men's times. In both cases, it appears from the scatter plot that the line fits better to the points than the line did in the scatter plot of the gaps.

Student 3:   The equation of the line for the women's time from my calculator is

$$\hat{y} = -0.0465x + 114.5, \text{ or } 114.5 - 0.0465 * \text{Year}$$

And the equation for the men's time is

$$\hat{y} = -0.0259x + 71.4, \text{ or, equivalently, } 71.4 - 0.0259 * \text{Year}$$

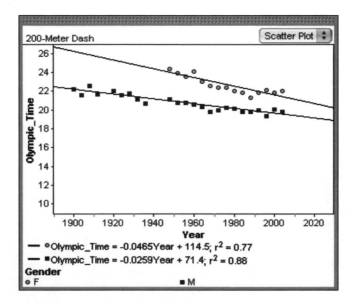

Fig. 3.4. Regression lines for men's and women's
200-meter Olympic times

Teacher: The representation $\hat{y}$ is used to indicate the predicted value of the winning time for men or women, using their respective regression lines. Using this symbol provides us with a way to differentiate between the predicted time, $\hat{y}$, and the actual time, y…. The 2008 winning time for females was 21.74 seconds. Veronica Campbell-Brown from Jamaica won this race. The winning time for males was 19.30 seconds. Usain Bolt, also from Jamaica, won this race. How close were our predictions based on our models?

Student 2: The 2008 time for women based on our regression line is

$$\hat{y} = -0.0465 * 2008 + 114.5 = 21.128,$$

or approximately 21.13 seconds. The 2008 time for men would be

$$\hat{y} = -0.0259 * 2008 + 71.4 = 19.393,$$

or approximately 19.39 seconds.

Student 1: We were off by approximately 0.61 seconds for the women's time and 0.09 seconds for the men. Our error in predicting the women's time is too large.

Teacher: Let's summarize our results. The slope for the line representing the women's time is –0.0465. Let's see…, the *y*-axis represents Olympic times, and the *x*-axis represents years. That means that the times represented by the line are *going down* about 0.0465 *seconds per year*. That would mean that the Olympic times are going down about 0.186 of a second, or about 0.2 of a second, between Olympics that are held every 4 years.

Student 3: For men, the slope is –0.0259. OK, so the Olympic times represented by this line are going down about 0.0259 of a second per year. That would mean men's times are going down about 0.1036 of a second, or about 0.1 of a second, between Olympics.

Student 1: So, women's times are going down faster, and that would mean that the lines would intersect…, and that would mean that there would be a time when the men's and women's times would be the same!

Teacher: We use the least-squares regression lines from our computer with a lot of faith that each of them represents a "good" line to make our predictions. Do you think the equations of the lines are a good way to make our predictions?

Student 1:   I think the equations are good, since they fit through the points. But none of these lines looks like it is a perfect fit.

Teacher: An interesting feature of the least-squares regression line is its very name. The equation of each of these this lines is determined by looking at something called the *residuals*. In our case, a residual is the difference between the observed time and the predicted time from our line. Try this out. What is the residual for the men's time in 2000?

Student 1:   The equation indicates that the winning time would be 19.60 seconds. The actual time is 20.09 seconds. So, the residual is the 20.09 seconds minus 19.60 seconds, or 0.49 seconds.

Teacher: Correct. And in this case, the residual is a positive number, since the actual time is greater than the time from the equation. Could it ever be negative?

Student 2:   Often! Each of the cases where the times are less than the times from the equation would be negative.

Teacher: Correct. To make sense of our equation, the computer squares the residual for each runner so that all the resulting numbers are positive and then adds them together. The result is that the squares of the vertical distances from the actual values to the predicted values are minimal. This is a good line to fit the data.

Student 3:   And then, for this particular equation, that sum is as small as you can get—or, the "least squares"! You're right; the name explains its fit.

Teacher: The result is a line that represents the data as a linear model. The more important question, however, is if the lines can be used to predict the future values and tell us when women and men will run about the same time. Perhaps there are other equations that would do a better job. For now, let's just discuss the equations of these lines and whether or not we think they fit the data to answer our questions.

Student 2:   We could determine when that might happen by solving the two linear regression lines for the common point…, or we could extend the graphs of the lines and estimate the point of intersection. Let's work with the graph [*see fig. 3.5, which extends the graph in fig. 3.4*].

Student 3:   It looks from the graph as though the lines meet around 2100. So, do we conclude that if Olympic games are held in 2100, we would expect the men and women to have approximately the same times in the 200-meter dash? When we used the gap times, we estimated that this would happen in 2076. I can see why they would not be the same then. In our gap summary, we were predicting when the difference between the men's and women's times would be 0. We were not really thinking that the recorded times would be going down—just the difference. Now, we are thinking that the times would continue to go down.

Student 2:   Wait a minute! If that were the case, it would also indicate that the Olympic times would be less than 18 seconds by then. Do you think that someone—male or female—could ever run 200 meters that fast?

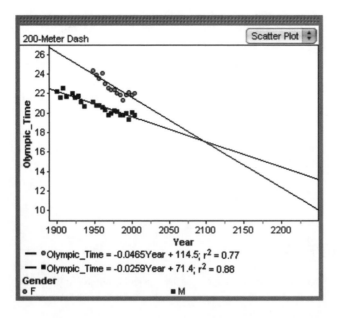

Fig. 3.5. A projection of men's and women's 200-meter Olympic times
into future Olympic years, based on linear regression models

Student 1:   That time does sound almost impossible—but records are always meant to be broken.

Student 2:   I think something else might be going on. Think for a minute: if we continue to extend the lines, eventually they will cross the x-axis. Look at this graph [*see fig. 3.6*].

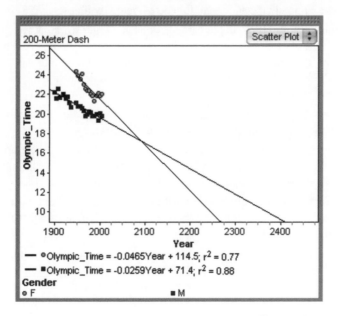

Fig. 3.6. A projection of men's and women's 200-meter Olympic times into
the distant future, based on linear regression models

Student 2: So, if the regression lines are accurate, then in approximately 2280 the winning Olympic time would be 0 seconds for females—and wouldn't the negative times after that mean the race is won before it starts! Obviously, something is not accurate.

Teacher: You created a regression line to summarize the scatter plot. A linear equation is generally a good starting point. For a limited range of data, it might be a good summary of the scatter plot. However, do you think the intersection of the regression lines is within that range? Is the future time that we are estimating results for outside of what is reasonable?

Student 1: The regression lines are based on the data in the tables. The estimate of when the female and male times might equal each other is almost 100 years after 2004. The scatter plot is based on a little over 50 years of recorded times. We might not see the same pattern of change in the next 50 to 100 years.

Extending the Task

Students might extend their reasoning with other models. The following dialogue shows how the preceding conversation might continue and progress:

Student 2: Clearly, there is something wrong with the linear model *over time*, since we never could get times close to—or even equal to—zero!

Teacher: Let's summarize your thinking. You created scatter plots and used linear regressions based on them to estimate when it might be possible that female and male gold-medal times in the 200-meter dash would be the same. Remember, if we use the regression lines, we are assuming that the future changes in the times will fit a linear equation.

Student 2: And a linear equation means that the changes in the 200-meter times would decrease at approximately the same rate for each 4-year Olympics.

Teacher: At some point in time, the linear equations no longer work, as you correctly pointed out—after all, the linear equations indicate a time many years from now when a person runs the race in zero seconds! The human body has limitations—we just don't know how those should enter into our thinking. Our initial question might be more meaningful to us now if we asked ourselves, When is the linear equation no longer accurate?

Student 2: And maybe we should also ask, Would the linear equation be accurate at the time when the female and male regression lines intersect?

Teacher: The linear equation would not work in the distant future, as there are no constraints on what those future times could be. The model that we need would indicate that the winning times would change in smaller increments over time.

Student 1: Yes, changes that would indicate that those new times in the future would differ by hundredths or thousandths of a second between Olympics rather than the current tenths of a second.

Teacher: Remember, linear equations are often used to start an investigation of a scatter plot. As we zoom out from the line, however, we realize that probably something other than a line would give a better suggestion of what happens to these times. We have a limited number of data points for this investigation—we probably are still within the linear range of the scatter plot.

Student 2: I think that athletes participate in the Olympics to win the race and possibly set a record. So, 100 years from now, they will still set records. But those records will be based on times that are closer to previous records.

Teacher: Could you sketch how you think the graphs of the men's and women's times would look in the future?

Student 1:   I think the graphs would look something like this [*see fig. 3.7*]. Also, I put a horizontal line to indicate that in the future I think both men and women will be getting closer and closer to a time, but there is a time that neither men or women will go under. I have no idea what that time would be! But I also think women will run faster than men as their rate of decline is greater.

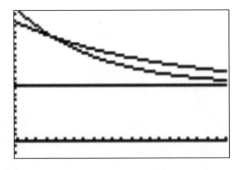

Fig. 3.7. A sketch of a curvilinear model projecting men's
and women's future 200-meter times

Teacher: Exponential models could represent your sketches. If we used an exponential equation, then the predicted times would be decreasing over time by a constant factor. Our previous work with geometry sequences indicated how each successive term of the sequence is determined by multiplying a given term by this factor. Because we hypothesize that the times are generally decreasing, this factor would be less than 1 if the models were connected to exponential functions. We could work with our computer software to estimate possible functions that look like the sketches that you created. The horizontal line is not part of the exponential model but is very important in our reasoning. What questions does the curvilinear graph [*student 1's sketch in fig. 3.7*] still pose to us?

Student 2:   I still do not think that the male and female times will intersect—I think the graph might look like this [*see fig. 3.8*]; however, I too see that there is a time that neither men or women will cross.

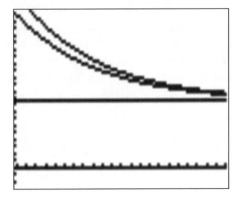

Fig. 3.8. A sketch of an exponential model projecting men's
and women's future 200-meter times

Student 3:   Whatever sketch, the point is that the Olympic times for males and females will be nearly the same in the future.

Students 1 and 2:   Agree!

Student 2:   But if we go with our graphs, there is a time that we suggest would "limit" the records—that would be our horizontal line. I wonder what that line is?

Student 3:   Well, we know it can't be zero!

Student 1:   I just don't think the record could go below 18 seconds, but I suppose the only way to know what that limiting time would be is to look at the data for the next 100 years or more!

Teacher: The details of your sketches will have to wait until we collect more data—and that will take time. What will be your predictions for the next Olympics in 2012?

Student 2:   I would use the regression lines to make my predictions, since I think 2012 is still within the range that makes the lines a good predictor of the future—after all, 2012 is only a few years away. My computer provides the equations of these lines. For males, my prediction would be approximately

$$(-0.0259)(2012) + 71.4 = -52.1108 + 71.4$$
$$\text{or} \approx 19.29 \text{ seconds.}$$

For females, I would make the prediction

$$(-0.0465)(2012) + 114.5 = -93.558 + 114.5$$
$$\text{or} \approx 20.94 \text{ seconds.}$$

Student 3:   The time predicted for males would be a record. If this happened, it would be a very small improvement over the record in 1996 of 19.32 seconds. The predicted time for females would also be a new Olympic record.

Student 1:   The steep rate of change in the female line would suggest that most future predictions would be record times.

Teacher: The future is very difficult to predict. To determine the most accurate model, we would need many more data points, so let's revisit this problem in about 100 years! In the meantime, let's continue to look at the different models that might indicate how this problem could play out in the future.

A Reflective Look Back for Teachers

As you focus on reasoning and sense making with your students, you may find it helpful to jot down observations and reflections in a journal. These can include questions that you have about your students' reasoning as well as thoughts on what you might do differently the next time you use the investigation with students to push them in their reasoning. In particular, for the Olympic games activity, you might consider recording your ideas in response to the following questions:

1.   How did the students connect the table to a graph?

2.   In what way did the students indicate that the values of the gap times as indicated by the regression line were not good predictors of the future gap times?

3.   In what way did the students interpret the slope of the regression lines in figure 3.4 to answer the initial question of whether women will ever run faster than men?

4. What was the primary concern that students communicated about putting faith in the equations of the regression lines as predictors of the future?

5. In evaluating the line generated by the computer software, what reasoning did the students use to decide whether the least-squares regression line and equation were a good fit for the data?

6. How did students think through the reliability of a regression line as a tool for looking many years into the future?

Chapter 4

Starbucks Customers—Designing and Analyzing an Observational Study

If you observe more female customers than male customers in your next visit to Starbucks, does that convince you that this majority exists in the general Starbucks population? This chapter presents an investigation that shows how students can move beyond descriptions of data to making inferential conclusions on the basis of their data. Consideration of sampling variability is critical in making sense of statistical studies.

The Context

In this investigation, students gather data on the gender of customers at a local store in the Starbucks Coffee chain. Students usually conjecture that females are more likely to drink coffee than males. Ideally, you can ask students to carry out the data collection at a nearby, familiar store. You can help them identify the particular population of interest (e.g., adults, high school students), depending on the perceived clientele. Students can then "test" the claim that a majority of this coffee-drinking population is female by using a simulation tool to generate a *sampling distribution*—that is, the distribution of the sample statistics from different random samples of the same size from the same population. The inference process in this investigation can be carried out rather informally to help students decide whether the data that they observed could have occurred simply "by chance."

Type of Investigation and Habits of Mind

The data discussed in this investigation were gathered from a Starbucks store on the campus of a university where females compose 43.6% of the student body. In the first part of this investigation, students consider issues in data collection, such as selecting a representative sample, disadvantages of a convenience sample, and measurement issues. Students try to balance the goals of using randomness in the sample selection with feasibility in collecting the data. Students should be given the opportunity to brainstorm and critique different possible designs. Once the group selects and agrees on a design, the students can collect the data.

After the data are collected, the students need to spend time exploring and even cleaning the data. Although the statistical methods are simpler for categorical data than for quantitative data, students need to be reminded to be very careful in their language, especially in "conditioning" the proportions involved in this study.

The second part of this investigation asks students to consider the plausibility of different values for the actual population proportion, given their sample result. This work requires students to make decisions in the presence of uncertainty and to consider issues of sampling variability. Table 4.1 identifies the key elements and summarizes the general reasoning habits and the specific statistical reasoning habits of mind that this investigation promotes.

Table 4.1
Key Elements and Habits of Mind in the Starbucks Exploration

Key Elements: Analyzing Data; Connecting Statistics and Probability

Habits of Mind

Analyzing a problem

Looking for patterns and relationships by—
- describing overall patterns in data;
- making preliminary deductions and conjectures.

Implementing a strategy

Selecting representations or procedures by—
- choosing and critiquing data collection strategies based on the question;
- creating meaningful graphical representations and numerical summaries;
- choosing a model;
- drawing conclusions beyond the data.

Monitoring one's progress

Evaluating a chosen strategy by—
- evaluating the consistency of an observation with a model;
- applying the iterative statistical process to the investigation.

Seeking and using connections

Connecting different representations by—
- understanding the sensitivity of an analysis to various components;
- connecting conclusions and interpretations to the context.

Reflecting on one's solution

Checking the reasonableness of an answer by—
- justifying or validating a conclusion by using inferential reasoning;
- looking for connections between the data and the context.

The Big Statistical Ideas

The main statistical ideas of this investigation revolve around the use of random sampling to make tentative conclusions about a larger population. Working with the investigation can help students formalize their intuitions about data collection procedures and lay a foundation for ideas of statistical significance and statistical confidence. This process involves generating hypothetical distributions for the sample results, pulled from various possible populations, to help students judge whether the actual observed sample result is consistent with the random sampling variability from that population. A big goal of this investigation is for students to develop an appreciation for the power of statistics to allow generalizations to a larger population from a smaller, but random, sample.

In the Classroom

This activity lends itself well to small- and large-group discussion, a teamwork approach to data collection, and exploration of hypothetical models for generating the data. Computer technology is very helpful in these explorations. The investigation can be carried out with students who do not have much prior statistical knowledge. It would be very useful to accompany this activity with one that focuses on sampling variability in general by asking students to generate multiple random samples from the same population. The discussion presented below is representative of a typical guided classroom discussion with about thirty-five students.

Summary of the task, and the statistical question

The dialogue below shows the development and unfolding of the investigation in the classroom. The teacher begins by eliciting interest in a class data collection project.

Part I: Collecting the data

Teacher: How many of you drink coffee? Do your parents drink coffee? Does just one of them drink it, or do both? Do you think either males or females are more likely to drink coffee? What about college students—do you think there is a difference in how often males and females drink coffee?

> **Note to Teachers**
>
> *Students will contribute different answers, personal stories, and conjectures about coffee drinkers. Students will often conjecture that females are more likely to drink coffee. In this study, students ended up exploring the gender breakdown of customers at Starbucks as an easy way to collect some data. However, you will continually need to remind students of the difference between the questions, "Are females more likely to drink coffee than males?" and "Are coffee drinkers more likely to be female?" The latter question is the one being investigated in this activity.*

Teacher: An advertising firm hired by the Starbucks store on campus is wondering whether the store should tailor its ads more to men or to women. How could we collect some data to help decide this?

Student A: Figure out whether more males or females drink coffee.

Teacher: OK, how are we going to do that?

Student A: Ask them!

Teacher: Ask whom?

Student A: Everyone who goes to that Starbucks.

Teacher: OK, but we have to be a bit careful. Do you want to investigate, "If you drink coffee, then are you more likely to be female?" or, "Are females more likely to drink coffee than males?" [*Teacher writes these questions on the board*]. Do you see the difference? How does this change how we will collect the data?

Student B: In the first one, we'd be sampling coffee drinkers and recording the person's gender. In the second one, we'd be sampling males and females in general and asking whether or not they drink coffee and comparing those two proportions.

Student C: Just because most coffee drinkers are female doesn't mean more females drink coffee?

Teacher: That's right—it doesn't. Why? Can you give an example where you get different answers? Where more coffee drinkers are female, but females are actually less likely to drink coffee than males?

Student D: If there are more females in the population. Say we have 100 females and 20 males, but only 30% of females drink coffee and 100% of the males do. Then we will see 30 females and 20 males in the store, but females are less likely to drink coffee as a group, since only 30% of them do.

Teacher: Well, it's easier to look just at Starbucks customers, so let's try that, and then we can always compare the gender breakdown among Starbucks customers to the breakdown in the population to see if there is a discrepancy.

Note to Teachers

It is important for students to understand that if most coffee drinkers are female, it does not follow that most females are coffee drinkers. To drive this point home even further, you might give your students a more extreme example. For instance, you might ask them to consider the question, "Are most professional male basketball players over 6 feet tall?" versus the question, "Are most males over 6 feet tall professional basketball players?" Although most professional male basketball players are over 6 feet tall, it obviously does not follow that most males over 6 feet are professional basketball players.

Student B: So first we want to figure out whether the Starbucks has more male or female customers.

Teacher: OK. How?

Note to Teachers

Matters that might come up. *Students may need some prompting to think about the details and logistics of a realistic data collection plan. The teacher gets this class of students to be very specific as they reason in dialogue. Many data collection plans would be quite suitable; the teacher's emphasis here is less on the final plan than on ensuring that students have thought about and debated many of the relevant issues involved in collecting data. In particular, the teacher makes certain that they see that taking a random sample of people and finding whether they drink coffee may be much more difficult than defining a more restrictive population, such as customers at one Starbucks. It is important for students to discuss the trade-offs in these various approaches.*

Student C: Don't the stores have records?

Student D: Not the gender of each person!

Student C: They have video cameras....

Teacher: Why can't we go over there right now and see who is in the store?

Student D: Sure!

Student E: You would need to gather a year's worth of data!

Teacher: I can't just look at one day?

Student E: No....

Teacher: Why not? [*Sensing student E's hesitation, the teacher prompts student F.*] What would you suggest?

Student F: We probably do need to collect data over several weeks because there are always different people coming into the store.

Teacher: Do I need to look at everyone that goes to the store?

Student G: No, but a lot of them.

Note to Teachers

Task implementation. *You might find that getting students to understand the usefulness and power of sampling can be difficult. Later in the lesson, you could consider showing your students how well sampling works in an extension of the task that focuses on the unbiased nature of random sampling. However, at this earlier point, you might want to focus more on the data collection details.*

Teacher: How many?

Students: [*Calling out different responses*] Like 100, 200....

Note to Teachers

Initially, students tend to believe that the size of the sample is the most important detail and that for a large population the sample size needs to be quite large. In general, they don't have much intuition about what sample sizes are "large"; instead, they usually pick round numbers that seem large to them.

Teacher: Well, I'm going to give you one week to collect the data. Do you want to record the gender of every Starbucks customer for that one week?

Students: [*Beginning to see their role in this data collection process*] No....

Teacher: So what can we do instead?

Student A: Just use a subset of the customers.

Teacher: OK. Let's consider "all Starbucks customers at this store" as our population [*writes on the board*], and let's take a *sample*—a subgroup of the population—and determine the gender of each person in the sample. Now, what would we like to be true about our sample?

Student A: We want it to look like the population.

Teacher: What is "it"?

Note to Teachers

It's important to prompt students to be specific in their language. Encourage your students to be precise, as this teacher does by continually asking students to identify the referent for "it."

Student B: The male-female breakdown in the group that we select should be similar to that of the Starbucks population.

Note to Teachers

The teacher in the example may have gotten lucky—the students appear to be grasping the purpose of sampling quickly and easily. However, this will not always be the case. You might need to point out the economic advantage of a sample and what you and your students hope a sample will tell you.

Teacher: [*Making a logical leap to get the students to react*] So, should we go from 10:00 to 11:00 every morning for a week and count the males and females in the store?

Students: No.

Teacher: Why not?

Student C: You'll just get the women who shop all day!

Student D: You won't get all the commuters who stop there on their way to work.

Student E: Won't all the women come together in one big group?

Teacher: Good thinking—so it won't be a very helpful sample if it leaves out entire segments of the population or overrepresents others! So how should we select the sample?

Students: Randomly.

Note to Teachers

Students often recognize the terms random *and* randomly *as important in describing or selecting a sample, but they may not fully understand the purpose of a random sample or the implementation of a random selection process.*

Teacher: And what do you mean by that?

Student E: Just go at lots of different times of day and on weekends and weekdays and make sure you get all the different types of customers.

Teacher: So time of day and day of week could be important, and we want to make sure we have a mixture? [*The teacher makes notes on the board here and later as the discussion continues.*]

Student F: Yes, and you will want to make sure that you have serious coffee drinkers and casual coffee drinkers and so on.

Teacher: It is a little hard, though, to know what all the different types of customers will be in advance. If we knew that, we wouldn't need the sample! We would like a method that will probably do that, even without our knowing what those "types" are. We also need the method to be practical—something we can carry out in the next week, so we can't camp out there 24/7, either…, OK, I want you guys to work in groups for the next few minutes and discuss a way to collect data next week as a group on the gender of Starbucks customers.

Note to Teachers

Matters that might come up. A number of issues might surface as the students develop their strategies. One strategy to be on the lookout for is the idea of going to the store and counting everyone who is there at one time. This would overrepresent those who stay in the store for longer periods of time, doing homework and so on, compared to those who take out their orders. For example, if staying in the store is more of a tendency that women exhibit than men, then the strategy would inflate the proportion of women in the sample.

If you do ask students to focus on a local Starbucks outlet, then you will also want to raise issues about where the store is located (e.g., in a shopping mall). The students should consider how the location might affect the population.

Students might also want to suggest other variables. What if the outlet mostly serves students from the school itself? Students conducting the investigation might ask whether a difference exists between freshman and senior coffee drinkers at the store. You could help students consider a stratification method (e.g., sample 50 from each class-rank), but those variables might be hard to classify in advance and might not be strongly related to the response variable of interest (gender) and thus might not be worth the extra work.

Students might also wish to consider the sample size, and they might suggest sampling, say, 15% of the population. You could point out to them that when the population is large, the relevant factor is the absolute size of the sample, not the percentage that the sample represents of the population. An extension described at the end of this task addresses this point in more detail.

Students seem to like suggesting a form of "systematic sampling" as opposed to a more formal random sampling method that would number every customer and randomly choose a subset. Systematic sampling still feels random to them and is much more convenient for this type of sequential data with a fluid population of unknown size. You might also want to emphasize the advantages of spacing out the observations to avoid collecting data on groups of customers that know each other.

After some discussion in groups, the students reconvened as a class and shared and compared strategies. The class then decided to randomly select some 30-minute periods throughout the week and have an observer record the gender of every tenth customer entering and buying coffee.

Note to Teachers

Task implementation. *After your students have brainstormed and presented their data collection approaches to the class, spend some time together comparing the different plans and the sample sizes that different groups recommend and their justification for their choices. In the course of the discussion, your students might agree on a particular plan, or you could allow different groups to carry out different sampling plans and then later discuss and compare the results.*

Teacher:	OK. So we have developed a method for selecting which customers we will observe. Are there any other considerations?
Student H:	What if someone enters the store, but then doesn't order coffee?
Teacher:	Good question. Will we count that person in the sample?
Student I:	Only the people who actually order coffee—and make sure it's coffee and not just coffee cake or tea.
Student C:	So you will have to be close enough to hear what they order.
Student J:	What about the people who just fill their cup without actually placing an order?
Student K:	You have to count them too—just make sure they are new customers and not refills.
Teacher:	OK, and how are you going to decide whether you have seen this person before or not?
Student J:	You can jot down their clothing when you record the observation.

Note to Teachers

Task implementation. *The teacher in the example was making notes on the board as issues arose. Such notes become useful once students have settled on a plan. Then it is important to write up a protocol for everyone to follow, with different individuals assigned different times to collect the data. You could also suggest other variables for your students to collect data on at the same time.*

Part II: Analyzing the data

After the students have collected data—in the example, they collected data on 260 customers, 154 females and 106 males—the reasoning dialogue can focus on any unexpected issues that arose or particular observations that the students made during the data collection process. Ask your students whether they want to consider removing any unusual observations from the data set, and then make sure they have a reasonable basis for doing so (they should not remove an observation simply because it is unusual but perhaps because there is reason to believe that it is in error or from a different population). A sample taken over several days and time periods should give the students a reasonable snapshot of the customers at that site. Their focus should then shift to exploring the data and considering what they can say about the population on the basis of what they observed in the sample. The dialogue below illustrates the data analysis process.

Discussing the sample results

Teacher: All right, what did we learn from our data?

Student A: There were more females than males among our Starbucks coffee drinkers.

Student B: More than half.

Teacher: [*Aiming for greater precision in language*] More than half what?

Student B: More than half of the customers are women.

Teacher: Good. So are women more likely to go to Starbucks then men?

> ### Note to Teachers
> By asking if women are more likely to go to Starbucks than men, the teacher probes the students' understanding of the question under investigation. This misstatement of the research question is typical of students, so if they don't suggest it themselves, you might want to bring it up for their scrutiny.

Student C: No, we didn't ask people in general whether or not they drank coffee, but we can say, "Among coffee drinkers, most were women."

Teacher: And we have to be careful that we don't overstate our conclusion here. Over half of those *that we observed….*

Moving beyond the sample

Teacher: Does this sample result convince you that more than half of all the customers at this store are female? What do you think the real percentage is—60%, 70%, 80%? How close do you think we are to the actual population percentage?

Student G: No, 80% is too high!

Teacher: How do you know that?

Student G: It's just too far away from what we got.

Teacher: OK, where is the cutoff? What values are too high, and what values are reasonable guesses for the population proportion of females?... So, what proportion of our sample was female?

Student C: Let's see…, 154 out of 260.

Teacher: And what is that as a decimal? Please get out your calculators and calculate it.

Student D: It's .592; how many decimal places do you want?

Teacher: Three is fine. So, about 59.2% of our sample was female. But we want to make a statement about the females in the whole population of customers—does our sample proportion convince you that more than half of all the customers at this Starbucks are female?

[*At this point, the teacher introduces an "intervention," showing the students a pair of dice and asking for a volunteer to roll the dice again and again and to call out the sums. The dice appear to be normal but are designed to produce a sum of 7 or 11 on every roll.*]

Note to Teachers

To help your students think about the likelihood of their results, you could try a number of "interventions." To conduct the intervention in the example, it is easy to buy dice that appear to be normal but yield a sum of 11 or 7 on every roll. Like the teacher in the example, you can ask a student volunteer to roll the dice and call out the sum until the class begins to become suspicious of the results (usually after about five rolls). You can also probe their thinking about what is making them suspicious of the dice.

Student A:	Those are very unusual outcomes for the sum of two dice.
Teacher:	Why?
Student D:	We would expect more variability in the sums.
Student B:	Seven is a common value, but not all sevens in a row like that, and only two different outcomes appearing?
Teacher:	*Assuming* what?
Student A:	Assuming they are fair dice.
Teacher:	So let me ask you this question: *Assuming* that half of the population of customers was female and half was male, would it be surprising to get 154 females in our sample?
Student B:	With 260 customers, half would be 130, and 154 is not that far from 130.
Teacher:	Some of you are saying it is far, and some of you are saying that 130 and 154 aren't that different. How can we decide?
Student C:	We need a larger sample.
Teacher:	What would be the advantage of a larger sample?
Student C:	It should be more accurate.

Note to Teachers

Students often use the term accurate *very broadly, without a clear idea of what it means or how to measure or compare accuracy in a particular situation. In fact, they will find uses of the word* accuracy *that refer both to* precision *and* bias.

Teacher:	But what if you can't collect any more data and have to decide on the basis of this one sample? How can we decide how accurate we think we are—that is, how close we think our sample result (59.2% of 260 customers) is to the actual population proportion?

Note to Teachers

Matters that might come up. *Students will probably feel uncertain about whether they can say on the basis of their sample that a majority of the actual population of customers at the Starbucks store is female, and you will probably find some students on each side of the fence. You might want to force them to make a commitment (e.g., show of hands) to one decision (yes, there is a population majority; or no, there is not) to engage them more actively in the discussion. Now would be a good opportunity to allow students to talk in groups first and come up with an argument to share with the other groups. Students might begin to argue that the sample size is too small to say anything, so you could remind them that the sampling method should give them a representative sample and the goal here is to estimate how close they think the sample proportion is to the population proportion, taking the sample size into account.*

Possible sampling results, assuming a chance model

Teacher: Let's consider a simpler case. Suppose we recorded data for only 26 customers, but you thought the population was 50-50 male to female. Would you be surprised to get 15 females in your sample?

Student A: No, it's just a little different; your sample won't necessarily match your population proportion exactly.

Teacher: What about 17 students? 20 students? How can we investigate whether these are surprising outcomes, like with the dice, assuming the population is 50% female?

Student B: Well, if it was 50-50, then that would be like tossing a coin. If I toss a coin 26 times, I expect 13 heads but could get anywhere from—I don't know—11 to 17 heads?

Teacher: That is exactly the right question. So what I want each of you to do is toss a coin 26 times and record the number of heads. Let's see how variable those results are!

Note to Teachers

Task implementation. *Have students determine the number of heads in 26 tosses and then pool the results on the board at the front of the class. The point is to have students see that this variation has a predictable pattern. Depending on the time available and number of students in your class, you can ask them to repeat the coin tossing two or three times or do the coin tossing outside of class and bring their results to class the next day.*

Teacher: So what does this tell us?

Student A: Most of us got around 13 heads.

Student C: But some were as few as 8 or as large as 19.

Teacher: So, suppose your friend comes along and says he found a way to make his coin tosses land heads more often than tails. You ask him to toss 26 times, and he gets 20 heads; do you believe him?

Student A: Sure, that's a lot more than half.

Teacher: But how do you decide that on the basis of this picture?

Student B: It would be surprising to get that many heads if he was just tossing the coin randomly, so we are convinced that something funny is going on here, like with the dice.

Teacher: OK, then how do we extend this same type of reasoning to our sample of 260 customers? Is it possible that 50% of the population of customers at this store is female and 50% is male, and you just happened by coincidence to get more females in your sample?

> ### Note to Teachers
> *Observe that the teacher explicitly states the inferential question that the students need to focus on: Could the sample of 260 customers with 154 females have happened by chance from a 50-50 population of females to males?*

Students: It's possible.

Teacher: So how can we decide whether our sample result is different enough from 50-50 to convince us that there is something "funny" going on?

Student D: Toss a coin 260 times.

Teacher: What will that tell us?

Student D: How often we find 154 heads.

Teacher: Yes, but we are going to let the computer do the tossing for us instead.

> ### Note to Teachers
> ***Task implementation with technology, and some conceptual issues.*** *Using technology in implementing a task such as examining the likelihood of getting heads 154 times out of 260 tosses involves some conceptual issues. Lots of different technological tools can be used (graphing calculator sampling tools, computer software that allows drawing repeated samples from known population proportions, and so forth). In the dialogue, the teacher and students discuss using a coin-tossing applet to generate some sampling distributions of sample proportions of females in repeated samples of size 260. This work involves yet another level of abstraction for the students, who must think of each coin toss as representing a person's gender. Be sure to remind your students continually of what the coin tossing represents in the simulation. Later on, this investigation uses the coin-toss simulations to move to hypothetical population proportions that are different from just 50-50, and to test those as viable candidates for yielding a .592 sample proportion.*
>
>   *Notice that the investigation treats the data as collected through a simple random sample even though a systematic sampling method may actually have been used. This is a reasonable approximation. A more sophisticated sampling method (e.g., stratifying) would result in even less sampling variability.*

Teacher: I'm going to use this applet to toss a coin 260 times, once for each customer. If I get heads, that customer is a female; if I get tails, that customer is male. Then we can count how many females we have in the sample of 260 customers, and we actually will report the proportion of females for each sample. In particular, it's easy to repeat this process of sampling from a 50-50 population many, many times, unlike the actual study, where we don't know the actual population proportion.

OK, the first time I got heads on 53% of the 260 tosses. [*Notes this value on the board.*]

The second time I got .42 heads, then .50 the third time. How many heads do you expect to see in 260 tosses?

Students: Well, 130, or .5.

Teacher: OK, that's fairly consistent with what I'm getting there. [*Lists a few more results from the applet: .48, .46, .51, and .50.*] So, what are we learning here?

Student K: The outcomes change every time.

Teacher: The values of the sample proportions definitely vary from sample to sample.

Student D: The values are all over the place.

Note to Teachers

Observe that the teacher is modeling more sophisticated language in these descriptions, giving students an opportunity to pick up the terminology naturally and use it. Furthermore, even if your students don't state explicitly that "the values are all over the place," as student D does, presenting a graph of some of the results might be valuable at this point or soon afterward.

Teacher: So let's see what we have so far: .53, .42, .50, .48, .46, .51, .50…. Let's make a graph—a dot plot—here [*see fig. 4.1*]. What do I want to call this graph? What is my variable along the horizontal axis? This is a graph of what?

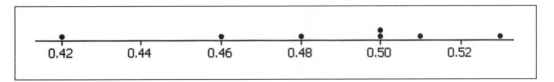

Fig. 4.1. A dot plot of sample proportions of heads (females) in
260 coin tosses simulated by an applet

Note to Teachers

It is essential that students identify and continually think in terms of the variable represented in the graph. Students should also be constantly thinking about what each dot represents in relation to a set of 260 coin tosses.

Student E: Coin tosses.

Teacher: Not quite, what was .42, .46, ….

Student D: The proportion of the tosses that were heads—females in our case.

Teacher: So, for each set of 260 tosses, I recorded the proportion of heads, or, I should say, the proportion of the 260 customers that were female. So we can label this axis "Sample Proportions" [*labels the axis on the plot on the board before continuing*]. So, let me add a few more dots by running the applet a few more times [*see fig. 4.2*].

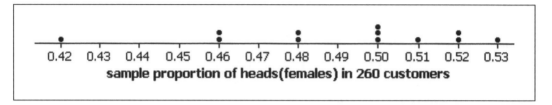

Fig. 4.2. The dot plot of sample proportions from figure 4.1 with more values

And here are a few more…. [*The teacher continues generating samples and adding five dots at a time to fill out the distribution; see fig. 4.3.*]

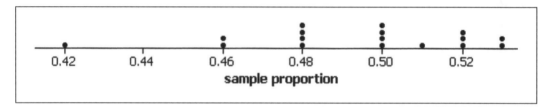

Fig. 4.3. More values on the dot plot from figure 4.2

And a few more…. [*See fig. 4.4.*]

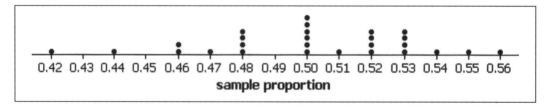

Fig. 4.4. More values on the dot plot from figure 4.3

So now let's look at 50 repetitions of recording the sample proportion of females in a sample size of 260 [*see fig. 4.5*].

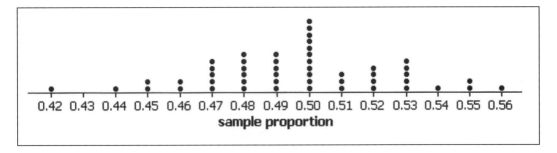

Fig. 4.5. Sample proportions of heads (females) in 50 repetitions of
the applet's simulation of 260 coin tosses

What are you noticing about these sample proportions?

Note to Teachers

In adding dots to the plot showing sample proportions of females in simulated samples of 260 customers, the teacher in the example takes care not to let students lose sight of where the dots are coming from and what they represent. You might prod your students with questions along the way, such as, "What does it mean to have gotten a .42?"

Student L:	They are clumping in the middle.
Teacher:	Where is the middle?
Student B:	Most of the observations are around .5.
Teacher:	Does that surprise you?
Student D:	We were expecting to get values near .5.
Teacher:	Why were you expecting to get sample proportions near .5?
Student F:	Because it's 50-50.
Teacher:	What is 50-50?
Student G:	Males and females, that's what we set the applet for, a 50-50 population to draw samples from.
Teacher:	Yes, we told the applet that the population was 50-50, so we expect to get results (sample proportions) closer to .5 rather than further from .5…. OK, let me jump to 1000 different samples of 260 people. Here are the 1000 different sample proportions [*shows the graph in fig. 4.6*]; let me also calculate the mean and the standard deviation. So, let's see; the mean is .408, and the standard deviation is .031. What do you notice about this distribution? Is there a pattern?
Student G:	Yes, the results are clustering around .5, and most of them cluster between .44 and .56, or about .06 on either side of .5.
Teacher:	Good. Even though these outcomes are random, they are not completely haphazard; they have a pretty predictable pattern. What does the pattern tell us?
Student K:	Most are between .44 and .56.

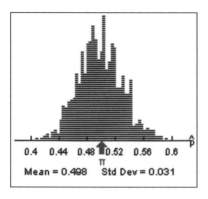

Fig. 4.6. A graph of the proportions of heads (females) in
1000 simulations of 260 coin tosses

Note to Teachers

The response that most of the outcomes are between .44 and .56 is an important one to emphasize and pursue because it demonstrates good insight into the sampling variability and supplies important information for accomplishing the task's goal of deciding how far the sample proportion can lie from the population proportion "just by chance."

Student C:	It's centered on .5.
Teacher:	What does that tell you?
Student D:	That there is not a preference.
Teacher:	What do you mean?
Student F:	That the population is 50-50.
Teacher:	Which population? Are you saying that the Starbucks customer population is 50% female?

Note to Teachers

At this point, many students will agree with the statement that the population of Starbucks customer is 50% female. But the teacher wants them to recognize the difference between the simulation, which was set up to be 50-50, and the actual population with an unknown proportion. Students will often interpret the finding that the center of the distribution is near .5 as evidence that the population is .5—or even that the sample result was wrong. You should continually emphasize what is "known" and what is "hypothetical" and that the students should trust their data.

Teacher:	Be careful here—we set up the simulation by using a fair coin, so we knew it was going to be 50-50. The question is whether the actual sample proportion result, .592 of

our Starbucks customers, is consistent with a 50-50 population. So, how surprising is it to get a sample proportion like .592 if we know the population proportion is .5?

Student D: Pretty surprising. There weren't many values near .592 in the simulated distribution. Most of the sample proportions were between .44 and .56.

Teacher: Right, when we have a 50-50 population, we seldom get results like .592 for a random sample of 260 people, just by chance, so, it is an unlikely outcome from a 50-50 population of men and women [*repeats this logic several times and even writes it on the board*]. So, what do we conclude from this?

Student C: A sample proportion of .592 seems unusual with a population that is 50-50 males and females.

Student D: So this gives us some reason for thinking that this sample proportion did not come from a 50-50 population.

Teacher: Now, this doesn't completely answer one of our original questions of whether males or females are equally likely to drink coffee, but we could consider testing another population proportion other than 50% female. The administration of our school recently announced that 43.6% of all our students were female. What does this tell you?

Student B: The sample proportion of females at Starbucks is even higher when compared to 43.6%!

Student E: There are more women going to Starbucks than in the population.

Teacher: Or at least there is a higher proportion of women. There appears to be a significantly higher proportion of Starbucks customers that are female compared to the proportion of females in the whole student population. So what would be a better estimate for the proportion of all Starbucks customers at this store if it's not .436 or .5?

Student A: Something above .5.

Teacher: How far above? Be more precise.

Student L: Maybe .6?

Teacher: How could we test that? Let's look at our applet; how will the distribution of sample proportions change if the population proportion is .6?

Student J: It will shift to the right.

Teacher: Let's see. OK, I'm changing the population proportion to .6 in the applet and again generating 1000 samples of 260 customers. So, yes, it now centers around .6 [*see fig. 4.7*]. But the key question is, "Where is .592?"

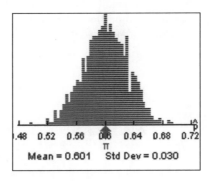

Fig. 4.7. The distribution of 1000 sample proportions when
the population proportion is .6

Student E:	Right there.
Teacher:	Yes, now an observation like .592 is very common when the population proportion is .6. So we would say that we have no reason to doubt .6 as the population proportion. Do you see the logic?
	[*Students tentatively nod.*]
Teacher:	What about .7? Would it be a good guess for the population proportion?
Student I:	Compared to .592?
Teacher:	Yes, is it possible that 70% of customers at this Starbucks are female, but we observed only 59.2% in our sample?
Student A:	Sure, I guess it's possible.
Teacher:	OK, so you think .7 is a reasonable guess for the population proportion? Well, we should "test" this as well. Let's put .7 in the applet. How will the distribution change?
Student C:	It will move to the right even more [*see fig. 4.8*].

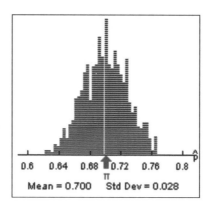

Fig. 4.8. The distribution of 1000 sample proportions when
the population proportion is .7

Teacher:	So what does this tell you?
Student D:	We don't see .592.
Teacher:	Right. So if the actual population proportion is .7, it would be highly unlikely to observe a sample proportion as small as .592. So we will say that .7 is not a reasonable guess for the population proportion. So then we might want to ask what range of population proportion values are reasonable.

[*The students work with the applet, and after some trial and error, they present their work.*]

Note to Teachers

Task implementation. *You might assign your students different population proportion values and ask them to generate the sampling distributions and see where .592 is on each one. If .592 appears in a "tail" of the sampling distribution, then that population proportion is not a believable value. A pool of all the results together can generate an interval of plausible values for the actual population proportion of females. If your students have access to the technology, this would be a good time to have them play with*

Note to Teachers—Continued

the applet themselves. In the dialogue that follows, after some trial and error, the students determine an interval of plausible values from around .54 on the low end to .64 on the high end. Their identification of this interval involves using 2.5% as the cut-off tail on each end of the sampling distribution. In this work, students' answers might vary a bit as a result of simulation error, but the goal is to get in the ballpark.

Students: If .65 is the population proportion…. [*They show the graph in fig. 4.9.*]

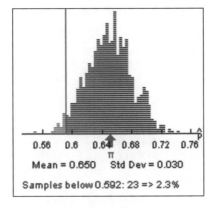

Fig. 4.9. The distribution of sample proportions (females) in 1000 simulations of samples of size 260 when .65 is the population proportion

If .64 is the population proportion…. [*The students show the graph in fig. 4.10.*]

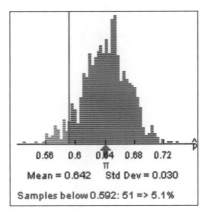

Fig. 4.10. The distribution of sample proportions (females) in 1000 simulations of samples of size 260 when .64 is the population proportion

So, .64 seems believable as the population proportion, but not .65, since .592 is inside the lower 2.5% of the sample proportions—the lower tail—for a population proportion of .65. On the other end, if .53 is the population proportion…. [*They show the graph in fig. 4.11.*]

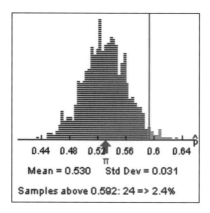

Fig. 4.11. The distribution of sample proportions (females) in 1000 simulations of samples of size 260 when .53 is the population proportion

If .54 is the population proportion…. [*They show the graph in fig. 4.12.*]

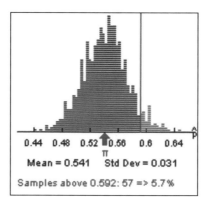

Fig. 4.12. The distribution of sample proportions (females) in 1000 simulations of samples of size 260 when .54 is the population proportion

So, we probably don't want to go as low as .53, since .592 is in the upper 2.5% tail for a population proportion of .53.

Drawing conclusions from the simulation process

Teacher: From our simulations, a value between .54 and .64 is a reasonable guess for the population proportion, based on observing the sample proportion of .592. Notice that this range definitely does not include .5, and certainly not .436. Even though we don't know the exact population proportion, we are pretty sure that a higher proportion of Starbucks customers are female than in the school population—somewhere between .54 and .64.

> ### Note to Teachers
>
> ***Important lessons from this task.*** *You might want to point out to your students many of the important lessons learned from the data collection process in this task. For example, you might discuss the limitations on the population (e.g., customers vs. coffee drinkers, this store vs. all Starbucks stores), and the initial sample analysis (most customers are females vs. most females are customers). If you ask students to write a report about this study, make sure that they critique the data collection process, and suggest some future directions for research (e.g., other variables of interest) as well as conjectures that they could test, such as, "Does the Starbucks store have more decaf drinkers in the morning?" Or, "Do females buy more lattes than males do?" Some of these data could be gathered by collecting a random sample of receipts rather than by observing individuals.*

Where to Go from Here: Building toward Confidence Intervals

After working through the investigation, students may be interested in learning about a more automatic way to generate confidence intervals and a way to calculate the "plus or minus" part of a result reported in the media. The following classroom dialogue illustrates an informal approach to this process.

Teacher: In fact, the interval can be found by taking $.592 \pm .05$ or so. What if we had sampled only 130 customers but had the sample proportion of .592? How would this change our analysis?… Take a few minutes, and repeat this analysis, using the technology. Generate sampling distributions for various assumed population proportions but with only 130 "coin flips" this time.

[*Students get roughly .51–.68, or .592 $\pm$ .09.*]

Teacher: So how does this range compare to what we found before?

Student A: It's wider.

Teacher: So what does that tell us?

Student B: We still have a population proportion of females that is above .5.

Teacher: Yes, what else?

Student C: We are now less certain of the real population value, because our interval is wider.

Teacher: That is a good way to think about it. There is less *precision* in our estimate, although with an interval of 51% to 68%, I'd say we have still narrowed things down quite a bit…. What if we had only 65 customers?

[*The students repeat the analysis with only 65 "coin flips" and get roughly .46–.71, or about .594 $\pm$ .12.*]

Teacher: OK, so wider still. So the sample size plays a very important role in what we can say about the population. In fact, what do you notice about .5?

Student G: This time .5 was actually inside the range!

Teacher: What does that tell you?

Student A: It's possible to get a sample proportion of .592 when the population proportion is .5, if the number of observations in our sample was only 65 customers in the first place.

Teacher: That's right, if it's a smaller sample. So, what relationship do you see here? [*Writes on the board.*]

        With sample size 260   the half-width of our confidence interval was .05

        With sample size 130   the half-width was .09

        With sample size 65   the half-width was .12

Student A: When the sample size was halved twice, we got a half-width that was more than twice as big.

Teacher: What if I wanted to estimate the population proportion within about 2 percentage points—that is, $\pm 2\%$—what sample size would I need?

Student B: About 1000? Wow, that's a lot.

Teacher: Very good. In fact, what if we calculate $1/\sqrt{n}$ in each case? [*Uses a calculator and writes on the board.*]

    Sample size $n = 260$ interval half-width .05 $1/\sqrt{n} = .06$

    Sample size $n = 130$ half-width .09 $1/\sqrt{n} = .088$

    Sample size $n = 65$ half-width .12 $1/\sqrt{n} = .12$

This gives us a rough, rough sense of how the width of the interval changes. If we want to cut the interval width in half, we need to quadruple the sample size!… So, suppose I want to take a random sample of the entire United States and ask the people in the sample their opinion about—say, whether they prefer cats or dogs—how large a sample size do I need to get within 3 percentage points of the population proportion? [*Uses a calculator and writes on the board.*]

$$1/\sqrt{n} = .03 \text{ gives } n \approx 1100!$$

We need only—randomly, of course—sample 1100 people! Now, that doesn't seem like such a large value, because we are talking about the entire U.S. population. But what I'm trying to tell you is that the population size doesn't really matter. As long as we take a sample that is random enough, the sample size will tell us how accurate we are!

A reflective look back for teachers

As you focus on reasoning and sense making with your students, you may find it helpful to jot down observations and reflections in a journal. These can include questions that you have about your students' reasoning as well as thoughts on what you might do differently the next time you use the investigation with students to push them in their reasoning. In particular, for the Starbucks activity, consider recording your ideas in response to the following questions:

1. Students often think that every individual and every variable must be measured. Do you think that your students recognize that a random sample, although not perfect, should be able to give a reasonable idea of what is going on in the population?

2. Do you think that your students could now read a report of a national poll in the newspaper and have an idea of what is involved when the $\pm$ interval for a population proportion is reported?

3. Were your students able to understand the purpose of generating hypothetical distributions? How could you help make the usefulness of those distributions clearer to them? What would motivate them to want to look at hypothetical samples from a known population?

4. Students often think that a study must be repeated many, many times before anyone can learn anything. Although replication is good, do your students realize that they can say a lot on the basis of just one study, with a corresponding measure of uncertainty to their claims?

5. What additional cautiousness or skepticism would you like your students to exhibit when they read reports of published surveys or polls?

6. Where in your curriculum would it make sense to ask students to complete this task?

7. If you were to use this task again, what would you do differently?

Chapter 5

Memorizing Words Revisited — Is the Treatment Effect Real?

Another common source of data is randomized experiments or clinical trials. But how can we tell whether a difference that we observe between two groups in an experiment is large enough to convince us that there is a genuine treatment effect beyond the "noise" in the data?

The Context

This activity involves a very simple study that can be conducted in class to illustrate many components of an effective experimental design. Students are randomly assigned to two groups and asked to memorize words on a list. The words for one group are meaningful and easily recognized by the students, and the words for the other group are nonsensical. The students use data that they collect on themselves, and as a result they become all the more invested in the outcome of the study!

Extending examples in *Focus in High School Mathematics: Reasoning and Sense Making*

Examples 19 and 22 in *Focus in High School Mathematics: Reasoning and Sense Making* (NCTM 2009) present data on the numbers of meaningful words and nonsense words remembered by two groups of ninth-grade students that received different lists of 20 three-letter words to memorize. One group's list consisted of meaningful words, and the other group's list consisted of nonsense words. The difference between the mean numbers of words remembered (meaningful vs. nonsense) was 4.27.

This result provides some evidence that students tend to do better when memorizing meaningful words than when memorizing nonsensical words. Another possible explanation is that more students who were generally better memorizers ended up in the "meaningful words" group. Because the students were randomly assigned to the two groups, this shouldn't be the case, but we don't know for certain. How can we explore whether preexisting differences between the two groups, rather than the list and type of words that each group saw, could explain the better performance of the meaningful words group?

Type of Investigation and Habits of Mind

Students often hear reports of differences between groups, but sorting out the "real" differences can be difficult. For example, an increase in students' test scores could reflect a different studying strategy or could simply be an artifact of random variation in scores. Students need to develop their intuition about when and when not to get excited about a result. This investigation helps students understand how to detect *statistically significant* differences between two treatment groups in an experimental study. The reasoning of statistical inference is notoriously difficult for students, so the investigation uses a simulation approach that they may find more intuitive.

The first part of the chapter represents a classroom discussion that leads students to think about issues of statistical significance and how significance could be assessed. It is assumed students have had some exposure to random assignment as a method for creating similar treatment groups, thereby controlling for confounding variables in an experimental study. Table 5.1 identifies the key elements and summarizes the general reasoning habits and the specific statistical reasoning habits of mind that this investigation emphasizes.

Table 5.1
Key Elements and Habits of Mind in the Meaningful Words Experiment

---

**Key Elements: Connecting Statistics to Probability;
Interpreting Designed Statistical Studies**

Habits of Mind

Analyzing a problem

Looking for patterns and relationships by—
- describing overall patterns in data;
- analyzing and explaining variation.

Implementing a strategy

Selecting representations or procedures by—
- considering the random mechanisms behind the data;
- choosing a model;
- drawing conclusions beyond the data.

Monitoring one's progress

Evaluating a chosen strategy by—
- evaluating the consistency of an observation with a model;
- questioning whether the observations make sense within the problem context.

Seeking and using connections

Connecting different representations by—
- understanding the sensitivity of an analysis to various components;
- connecting conclusions and interpretations to the context.

Reflecting on one's solutions

Checking the reasonableness of an answer by—
- considering and evaluating alternative explanations;
- understanding the allowable scope of conclusions;
- determining whether a conclusion based on the data is plausible;
- justifying or validating the solution or conclusion by using inferential reasoning;
- analyzing and accounting for variability.

The Big Statistical Ideas

This investigation focuses on the pattern of chance variation that arises from randomly assigning subjects to treatment groups. After considering the amount of chance variation, investigators can probe the experimental results for evidence of a genuine *signal*—a treatment effect that could not have plausibly arisen from the random assignment process alone. The investigation exposes students to a very powerful simulation approach that can easily be extended to different scenarios while also developing their intuition about whether an outcome could have occurred by chance and what factors might affect that assessment.

In the Classroom

Tell students that you are going to collect some data from them. Make equal numbers of copies of two lists of words, randomly mix them ahead of time, distribute them face down to your students, and then tell them that when you say "go," they can turn over the page and try to memorize as many words as they can. Time them, giving them, say, 30 seconds, depending on the number of words. When time is up, tell them to stop, and ask them to turn over the paper and write down as many of the words as they can remember. Then ask them to exchange papers with a neighbor to "grade" each other's performance.

The students should not be aware that there are two different treatment groups. As much "control" as possible should be exerted to create uniform testing conditions. After the study is conducted, you can discuss with your students the principles of comparison, blindness, and random assignment exhibited in this study. Once the data have been compiled, share them with the students for analysis. If your sample sizes are extremely small, you may also wish to have some supplemental data available to combine with the data that the students generated.

Summary of the tasks, and the statistical question

A conversation such as the one presented below might take place after the class has examined both numerical and graphical summaries of the data—and in all likelihood has seen that the group receiving the meaningful words was more successful at the memorization task. In the dialogue below, the difference in the group means is 4.27 words, as in examples 19 and 22 in *Focus in High School Mathematics: Reasoning and Sense Making*.

> **Note to Teachers**
>
> **Task implementation.** *The classroom dialogue in the example focuses on means but could also have focused on medians. Medians are easier for "by hand" calculations but are less used in statistical practice because they often show some confusing irregularities in the randomization distributions. Exploring this point with technology would make a nice extension of this investigation—for an appropriate applet, see, for example, http:// rossmanchance.com/applets/randomization.html.*
>
> *In the investigation,* treatment *denotes the type of words (meaningful or nonsense) that the students received for memorization, and* treatment effect *is the* difference, *on average, between the numbers of meaningful words and nonsense words that the students remembered.*

> **Note to Teachers—Continued**
>
> Note that the students in the dialogue are using very good reasoning rather quickly. The ideas in this activity might actually take your students a while to grasp and become comfortable in using. However, it is important to let them struggle with the approach. Using dice as in the dice example in chapter 4 is one way to convince them that the logic that they need to use is not unnatural!

Engaging students in the exploration

It is definitely worth spending some time building students' understanding of the usefulness and relevance of the simulation that will be conducted in this investigation; see also chapter 4 on prompting students to consider looking at data from a known model to help them judge the observed data.

Teacher:	Let's begin by assuming that the *treatment*—giving students meaningful words vs. giving them nonsense words—does not make a difference in how many words are memorized. Is it still possible that we would end up seeing a difference in the mean number of words memorized in the two groups?
Students:	Yes.
Teacher:	Why?
Student A:	The instructions could have been delivered differently to the two groups.
Student B:	Maybe the meaningful words group was trying harder for some reason?
Teacher:	True. But what if the instructions were delivered to the two groups at the same time, and the students didn't even realize that two different lists were given out?

> **Note to Teachers**
>
> Observe that the teacher in the dialogue begins by pointing out all the controls that were used in the actual study to try to eliminate as many extraneous variables as possible.

Student C:	Maybe it's easier for students to memorize the meaningful words.
Teacher:	Yes, that is what the researchers are trying to find out. So, do these results convince you that giving students meaningful words will, on average, *cause* them to remember more words, or could there be another explanation for what these researchers observed? For example, could the meaningful words group have tended to receive higher scores even if memorizing meaningful words wasn't any easier than memorizing nonsensical groupings?
Student B:	Some students are better at memorizing than others.
Teacher:	True, so there is definitely going to be variability in the scores between students. Good. But why would that lead to a difference between the two group means like the difference that we observed?

Note to Teachers

The teacher draws the students' attention to the key issue—the inescapable alternative explanation: maybe the researchers just got unlucky in the random assignment, and more of the better memorizers ended up in the meaningful words group than in the nonsense words group.

Student C: Maybe all the good memorizers ended up in the meaningful words group, like you said.

Student D: Or even just one or two really good memorizers ended up in the meaningful words group.

Note to Teachers

It is useful to try to get students to focus on a systematic pattern rather than on one or two people.

Student A: But the random assignment to groups is supposed to make the two groups look similar, right?

Teacher: Yes, but we still have to guard against getting unlucky. Is it possible that, even though we did the random assignment correctly, we ended up with some difference between the groups?

Students: Yes.

Teacher: Is it believable that this could result in a difference in the mean scores between the groups of 4.27 words?

Student D: I don't know.

Student B: It's possible—anything is possible—it's random.

Student D: Plus, it's not like everyone in the one group did better than everyone in the other group.

Teacher: OK, so we agree that it is *possible* for our data to look like this, even if the treatment—type of words that students were asked to memorize—really doesn't make a difference. But how do I decide whether a difference as large as we observed between the groups is *probable* in this scenario? Perhaps if I decide that it would be really, really surprising for the groups to differ by this much under random assignment, then I could convince the researchers that "random chance" is not a reasonable explanation for what they observed—a difference in means as large as 4.27.

[*The students express puzzlement about what the teacher means.*]

Teacher: OK, if I don't believe that the type of words given—meaningful vs. nonsensical— had any effect at all, and each student was going to obtain his or her same score no matter which group he or she was put in, how probable is it that I will get a difference in the means around 4.27 just from getting unlucky in my random assignment? How could I decide this?

[*Again the students are perplexed.*]

Teacher:	So, how do we decide whether the result that the researchers observed in the memorizing words study—a difference in means of 4.27—is surprising if we assume that there is no genuine treatment effect due to the types of words the students are given—meaningful vs. nonsensical?
Student D:	We need to know what types of outcomes are typical.
Teacher:	And what do you mean by "outcomes" here—how are we summarizing the results of this experiment?
Student D:	The difference between the two means.
Teacher:	Assuming what?
Student D:	Assuming there is no treatment effect?

Teacher: So we can repeat the random assignment process, assuming that the students' scores stay the same no matter which group they are put into, and explore how different the two group means tend to be from each other when we know for a fact that there is no treatment effect.

The simulation by the class

The simulation uses the memorization scores (below) from the study, and students perform the simulation in pairs according to the instructions that appear underneath the data. After following steps (*a*) and (*b*) to run the simulation and pool their results, they answer questions (*c*)–(*f*).

Students' scores

12, 15, 12, 12, 10, 3, 7, 11, 9, 14, 9, 10, 9, 5, 13
4, 6, 6, 5, 7, 5, 4, 7, 9, 10, 4, 8, 7, 3, 2

Directions

a.   Work with a partner and put the 30 scores above on 30 separate index cards. Shuffle the 30 cards and then deal out 15 to be group A. The rest will be group B. Determine the mean score of each group. Then calculate the difference in these two means (Group A – Group B).

b.   Pool your results with those of the other pairs of students in the class, with each pair putting one dot on the axis on the board for their value (Group A mean – Group B mean).

Questions

c.   Where are the values obtained from the simulations centered? Why does that make sense?

d.   Where does the researchers' result (a difference in means of 4.27) fall in this distribution of differences? Is a difference in means of 4.27 a likely or an unlikely occurrence?

e.   What conclusion would you draw from this study? In particular, which of the following conclusions do you consider more believable, and why?
   — There is no real difference between the treatments, and the researchers were unlucky in the random assignment to have found the difference of 4.27.
   — We are now convinced that there is a genuine effect from memorizing meaningful words instead of nonsense words.

f.   If the mean for the meaningful word group were only 2 words larger than the mean for the nonsense word group, what would you conclude? Be clear about how you have arrived at this conclusion.

Note to Teachers

Task implementation. *You can ask each student or pair of students to repeat the simulation several times—say, 2 or 3 times—to increase the number of repetitions. Spend some time having students describe the variable being measured in the graph and allow them to say how to label the horizontal axis.*

A typical discussion based on the simulation

In the dialogue that follows, the teacher and students reason about the graphs in figures 5.1 and 5.2.

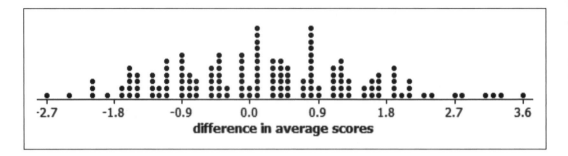

Fig. 5.1. Example results based on 150 repetitions

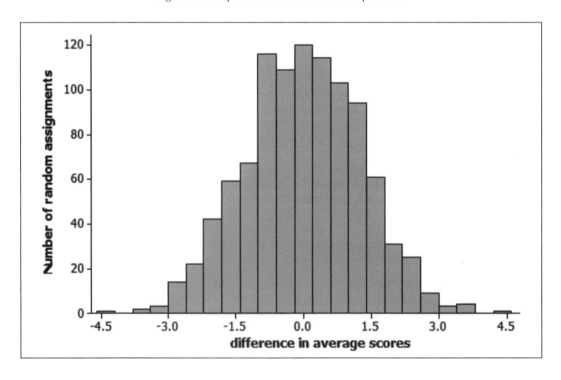

Fig. 5.2. Example results based on 1000 repetitions

Note to Teachers

Students will need some help in conceptualizing what graphs such as those in figures 5.1 and 5.2 reveal. If your students are working with a dot plot such as that in figure 5.1, ask them what each dot represents—what the observational units are. If the students are working with a frequency histogram such as that in figure 5.2, ask them to explain what an individual bar represents.

Teacher: Where are these values centered? Why does that make sense?

Student A: They center around zero.

Student B: Why?

Student A: Because we are assuming the groups are equal.

Student B: Oh, the random assignment should balance out the two groups, so the differences should be around 0.

Teacher: Yes, but what else do you notice?

Student B: We don't always get zero; sometimes there is a difference in the groups.

Teacher: Indeed, random assignment will not always create equal groups, and they may differ a bit even when we know for certain that no real treatment effect is present.

Student A: And it could be either group, just by chance.

Note to Teachers

The student's statement, "And it could be either group, just by chance," is not completely clear—what does "it" refer to in the statement? The teacher could have asked for clarification. However, the student appears to be generalizing from the symmetric shape of the distribution to say that a higher mean might occur in the scores of either group, just by chance. You could point out that the order of subtraction—which group mean is subtracted from the other—doesn't really matter when there is no treatment effect, as long as the students are consistent about which group's mean they take away (the order of subtraction) each time.

Teacher: Where does the researchers' result (a difference in means of 4.27) fall in this distribution? Is it an unlikely occurrence in this distribution?

Student A: Four doesn't happen very often.

Student B: Nor –4.

Student A: I guess we should just look at the positive 4, since group A here is the meaningful words group?

Student B: OK. So yes, it is a little surprising, because a difference of 4.27 never once came up in these 1000 values.

Teacher: What do these values represent? One thousand what?

Student B: One thousand students?

Teacher: No, where did each dot in the dot plot come from?

Student B: Each time we did a new shuffle.

Teacher: So, each time we do the hypothetical random assignment with the shuffle, we get a potentially different result, but the differences in the group means tend to be close to zero. And it is pretty surprising to a get a difference in the means as large as 4 if all that is going on is variation based just on random assignment.

Note to Teachers

*As you discuss the data from the simulation and help students understand their useful-
ness in analyzing the data from the word memorization study, continually emphasize
that the "random assignment" in the simulation is "fake" or "hypothetical" to distinguish
the shuffles that your students do from the data arising from the actual study.*

Teacher: OK. What conclusion would you draw from the study of word memorization? In particular, which of these conclusions do you consider to be more believable:

—   There is no real difference between the treatments, and the researchers were
unlucky in the random assignment to have found the difference of 4.27,

or,

—   We are now convinced that there is a genuine effect from memorizing
meaningful words instead of nonsense words?

Student A: It's unlikely for random assignment alone to lead to such a large difference.

Student B: Results like this don't happen very often by chance alone.

Student A: So I would say that it was due to the type of words instead of bad luck or coincidence,
since it would be pretty surprising to get a 4.27 randomly. It is rare to see a difference
this large between the groups, so we conclude that the meaningful words helped.

Note to Teachers

*The idea of "coincidence" seems to be one that students can relate to easily. Student A
is fairly confident about saying that the occurrence of a difference of 4.27 in the mean
scores of the two groups would be a highly unlikely "coincidence."*

Student B: But couldn't it be something else?

Teacher: Well, not really. If you believe in the random assignment, there really should not be
any major differences between the two groups except for the treatment that was im-
posed. So, if we decide it wasn't bad luck in the random assignment, the only really
plausible explanation left is that using meaningful words really did help the students
memorize more words.

Note to Teachers

*If researchers have confidence in a study's random assignment, they can be confident
that any major (statistically significant) difference observed in the results for two groups
is due to the treatment. You might want to ask students about this logic frequently. If your
students work with another prototype example, such as the dice in chapter 4, you can
refer to that example often as well and help them see the connections among different*

> **Note to Teachers—Continued**
>
> examples. After looking at their simulation results with the dice, students have to make a similar decision: Do they conclude that "the dice are fair" or that "something else is going on"?
>
> Students also seem to struggle with the distinction between probable and plausible. The goal is to convince them that an unlucky random assignment leading to a difference as large as 4.27 is so improbable that random chance alone is not a plausible (that is, believable or reasonable) explanation for what was observed between the group means for memorizing the words.
>
> Getting students to verbalize their understanding clearly, in relation to the context and by using appropriate terminology, is critical to their development of inferential reasoning. The next section of dialogue illustrates another way of reasoning about the results generated by the simulation.

Student C: From this graph [*see fig. 5.2*], clearly the treatment (type of words) doesn't matter.

Teacher: Why?

Student C: Most of the differences are around zero. The researchers must have done something wrong to get a 4.27.

Teacher: But in that graph [*see fig. 5.2*], we see what would happen *if we knew* that there was no treatment effect from the types of words used—meaningful vs. nonsensical. We caused the values to be close to zero because we set it up that way, to simulate the differences under that assumption that the type of words didn't matter. So, under that assumption, is a difference of 4.27 surprising in our graphical display?

Student C: Yes.

Teacher: So, since the hard-working researchers, in their properly conducted study, did observe a difference of 4.27, do you think that outcome came from an environment where there was no treatment effect, where students would do just as well with either list?

Student C: It would be surprising.

Teacher: What is "it"?

Student C: That large a difference in the group means.

Teacher: So instead of thinking they got that unlucky, we might be more comfortable concluding that our initial assumption of no treatment effect was wrong!

Student C: So we conclude that there is a treatment effect.

Teacher: We have strong evidence that there is—that the difference that we observed between these two group means didn't just happen "by chance alone."

> **Note to Teachers**
>
> One way to assess whether your students are understanding this type of inferential reasoning is to ask them to consider different values for the difference in group means.

Teacher: What if the meaningful words group mean was only 2 words larger than the nonsensical group mean? What would you conclude? Be clear about how you are arriving at this conclusion.

Student A: That could be just from the random assignment.

Student B: Yes, it's not so surprising.

Student A: The difference in means in that study would be different from zero, but not enough to convince us that there was a treatment effect.

Student B: The graphs [*see figs. 5.1 and 5.2*] show that a difference of 2 is pretty typical.

Teacher: *Even if* there were no treatment effect—hypothetical. So, while there could be an effect from the meaningful words, there wasn't strong enough evidence to convince us that we didn't get these unequal groups just from the random assignment process.

Note to Teachers

It is important to keep reminding students of the underlying assumption of no treatment effect behind the simulation.

Student C: This graph shows that a 2 is not a surprising outcome for the difference in the group means, and so that would be evidence that there is not a treatment effect.

Teacher: Well, or maybe better said, we don't have strong evidence against "no treatment effect." All we can say is that these results are not inconsistent with what we would expect to see when there is no treatment effect, rather than we have proven or supported the conclusion that there is no treatment effect.

Note to Teachers

Students will need some time to become comfortable with the conditional nature of their observations – that "a difference in group means of 4.27 is a surprising outcome if there is no treatment effect."

Again, consider the dice example in chapter 4, where rolls of the dice produced sums of only 7 and 11. That result is surprising only if the dice are fair. It would not be at all surprising if the dice faces consisted only of 6s, 5s, and 2s.

Where to Go from Here: An Extension of the Task

The task below first asks students to compare hypothetical results from other classes that conducted the same experiment. The discussion should lead students to consider issues of variability and sample size in experiments, along with the actual size of the difference in the group means, when they evaluate the strength of evidence of a treatment effect. Students can produce and examine the randomization distributions for these different cases to analyze the effects of sample size, effect size (between-group variability), and within-group variability for the "surprisingness" of the observed result.

Portraits of students' partial reasoning illustrate an understanding of the randomization distribution and how it helps in drawing conclusions about the original study. These conclusions may relate to the difference between the simulation results and the actual results, where the randomization distribution should be centered and why, what it means for the observed data to be in the tail of the randomization distribution, and so on. A culminating question asks students to suggest data that would be most convincing in a situation where an "ideal" answer has little to no within-group variation.

The task centers on comparing the dot plots in figure 5.3, but you might also be ready to provide your students with the numerical values (denoted by arrows in the dot plots) of the difference in group means in each case.

Extension task

The directions for students follow:

a. Suppose that the same study comparing group means for numbers of meaningful and nonsensical words memorized was conducted in three other classrooms. In each case, do you think the results for the new class would provide more convincing evidence or less that the meaningful words list was easier to memorize? Explain how you are deciding.

b. Create and analyze the randomization distribution for the two lists for the new class. How does this randomization distribution compare to the one for the original study? Is the *p*-value larger or smaller? Does this ordering make sense?

c. Make up 15 hypothetical results for the meaningful words group and 15 for the nonsensical words group that would help you to be very convinced that the meaningful words list made a difference. What factors are you considering in making your lists?

A discussion of reasoning about the results of a second class compared to those from the original study

In the following dialogue, the teacher and students refer to the dot plots in figure 5.3.

Original Study

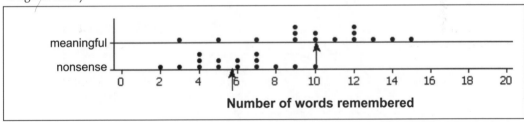

Class 2

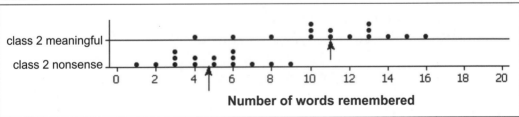

Fig. 5.3. A comparison of dot plots for the number of meaningful and the number of nonsense words memorized by two different classes

Student A: In class 2, there is more separation between the meaningful and the nonsense groups.

Student B: There is still some overlap.

Student A: Yeah, but now all but three students with the meaningful words list remembered more of the words than all of the students with the nonsense words.

Student B: So is that strong evidence that the type of words made a difference?

Student C: Look at the means in class 2—about 11 for meaningful and 4.8 for nonsense. They are much further apart [*than the means for the groups in the original class*].

Student B: If the difference in the groups is larger, then the evidence is stronger that the types of words really made a difference in this case.

[*The students look at the randomization distributions shown in figure 5.4.*]

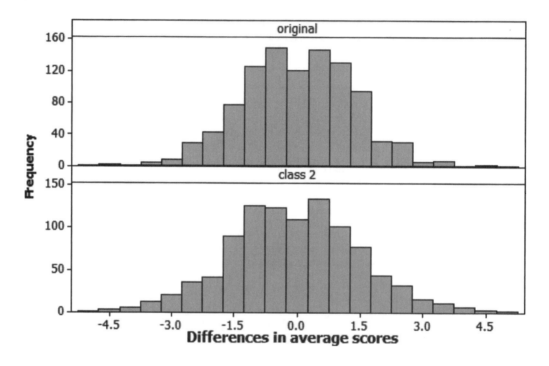

Fig. 5.4. A comparison of the randomization distributions for the difference in the mean numbers of meaningful and nonsense words memorized by two different classes

Student B: There is a bit more spread in the second case.

Student A: Yes, wouldn't that mean 4.27 is more likely?

Teacher: Keep in mind what you want to compare on this graph. Now you want to use the observed difference, $11.07 - 4.80 = 6.27$.

Student C: Oh, yes—that is way off the graph this time.

Teacher: So what does that tell you?

Student A: We would never see a difference like 6.27.

Teacher: If?

Student A: If the treatment did not have an effect.

Student B: Yes, this is strong evidence that the difference in the group means wasn't just due to the random assignment.

Student C: And it happened because the difference in the actual study was larger this time.

A discussion of reasoning about the results of a third class compared to those from the original study

In the following dialogue, the teacher and students refer to the dot plots in figure 5.5.

Original Study

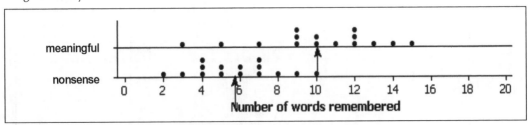

Class 3

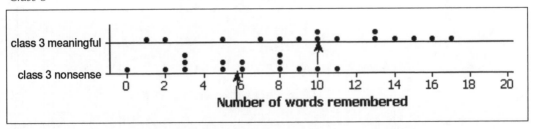

Fig. 5.5. A comparison of dot plots for the number of meaningful and the number of nonsense words memorized by the original class and a third class

Student A: I don't see as much of a separation between these two groups for class 3.

Student B: The meaningful group now has some pretty low scores, and the nonsense group did a bit better. They had more 8-to-12 scores this time. Still, the meaningful group had all the scores 13 and above.

Student C: There is less consistency in the group scores—no real modes this time.

Student A: The meaningful group still tended to do better, but not by as much. But the nonsense group still has more scores between 3 and 6. But the difference isn't as striking, since there are more lower scores with the meaningful words group. I would say there is *less evidence*.

Student C: What is the difference in means this time?

Student A: It's $10.07 - 5.80 = 4.27$; it's exactly the same!

Teacher: So, how else might you characterize the differences between the distribution for the original data and the distributions for class 3?

Student A: The scores are less clumped together.

Teacher: So, how does that affect your evaluation of the size of the difference in the group means?

Student A: When there is more spread in the data, you'd expect bigger differences in the groups even when there is no treatment effect?

[*The class is looking at the randomization distributions in figure 5.6.*]

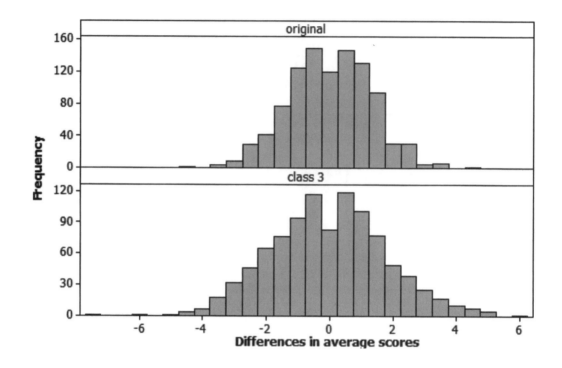

Fig. 5.6. A comparison of the randomization distributions for the differences in the mean numbers of meaningful and nonsense words memorized by class 3 and the original class

Student B: So, we see a little more spread in the class 3 values [*differences in average score*].

Teacher: And how you do feel about the observed difference in means of 4.27?

Student C: It's still rare, but I guess less so than it was before. Definitely less rare than for class 2.

Student A: So the evidence with class 3 would not be as strong as for class 2.

Student B: It's not quite as rare for the random assignment process alone to lead to a difference of 4.27. It's still strong evidence, just not as strong.

A discussion of reasoning about the results of a fourth class compared to those from the original study

In the following dialogue, the teacher and students refer to the dot plots in figure 5.7.

Original Study

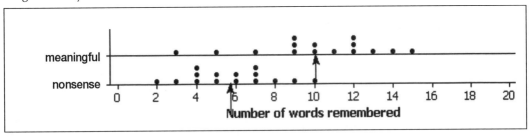

Class 4

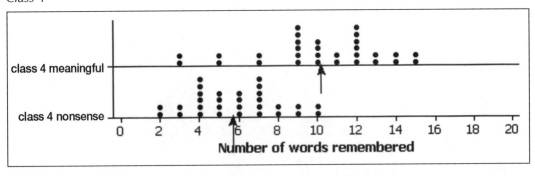

Fig. 5.7. A comparison of dot plots for the number of meaningful and the number of nonsense words memorized by the original class and a fourth class

Student A:	The meaningful words group still did better.
Student B:	And the means are the same, too. So we still just have a difference of 4.27.
Student C:	How is this scenario different from the original study?
Student B:	There are more dots?
Teacher:	So how will more students being involved in the study change things?
Student B:	Won't that make things more variable, more likely to get strange results?

Note to Teachers

Students often assume that more observations lead to more variable sample distributions.

Student C:	But we got the same means, and the spread is about the same as in the original data, so I don't think the evidence changes at all!
Teacher:	Perhaps. Why don't you look at the randomization distribution?

[*The class looks at the randomization distributions in figure 5.8.*]

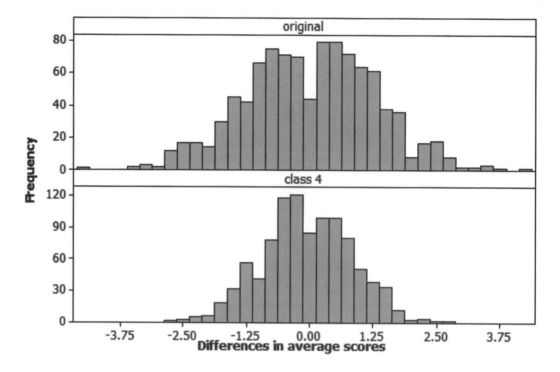

Fig. 5.8. A comparison of randomization distributions for the differences
in the mean numbers of meaningful and nonsense words memorized by class 4
and the original class

Student B: Wow, much less spread out.

Student A: The difference of 4.27 is now super-extreme. It would never happen "by chance." This
would actually give us pretty strong evidence that the treatment was effective.

Student C: So with larger sample sizes, the evidence is stronger.

> **Note to Teachers**
>
> **Discussion points.** *Most students pay attention only to one dimension at a time when
> comparing distributions (e.g., difference in centers). Even worse, they may pay atten-
> tion only to extremes while ignoring important distributional comparisons. Your students
> might need some encouragement to focus on variability—say, with class 2—and how it
> could affect the comparison. They might not have much intuition initially for the effect of
> sample size, but question (b) in the extension task can help them test and confirm their
> predictions.*
>
> *You might want to show the results for all four classes together to help students visu-
> alize the differences across the classes (see fig. 5.9). You could also ask your students to
> conjecture why results might differ like this across classes (e.g., why the results for one
> class might be much more variable than in another class).*

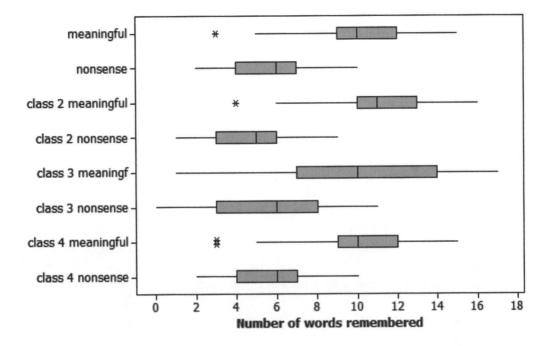

Fig. 5.9. Box-and-whisker plots showing results for all four classes in memorizing meaningful and nonsense words

Note to Teachers

Discussion notes. *Question (c) in the extension task asks students to make up 15 hypothetical results for the meaningful words group and 15 hypothetical results for the nonsensical words group that would help them be very convinced that the meaningful words made a difference. Push students to think about the centers of the distributions being different and small amounts of overlap between the distributions. Students who deeply understand the issue might create results with no within-group variability (e.g., all 5s in one group and all 10s in the second group).*

Additional extensions

Two additional tasks follow to extend students' reasoning about the results of the original study:

1. Suppose that the difference in *median* scores were 4 in the original study. How could you assess whether a median score difference of 4 is convincing evidence of a treatment effect? (What would you simulate?)

2. Suppose that the difference in the *medians* between the two lists is 4 words. Describe circumstances under which you would be convinced there was a treatment effect, and circumstances under which you would not be convinced. (Remember to take into account issues surrounding within-group variability and sample size.)

A Reflective Look Back for Teachers

As you focus on reasoning and sense making with your students, you may find it helpful to jot down your observations and reflections in a journal. These can include questions that you have about your students' reasoning as well as thoughts on what you might do differently the next time you use the investigation with students to push them in their reasoning. In particular, for the meaningful words activity, you might consider recording your ideas in response to the following questions:

1. Did students appear to appreciate the purpose of the hypothetical random assignments? How might you help them develop a better understanding of that?

2. Did students appear to appreciate the power of random assignment for allowing researchers to draw cause-and-effect conclusions?

3. Do students now have a better understanding of *statistically significant* results as results that would not be likely to happen by chance alone?

4. Where in your curriculum would it make most sense to ask students to complete such a task?

5. If you were to use this task again, what would you do differently?

Chapter 6

Soft Drinks and Heart Disease— Critiquing a Statistical Study

As citizens and consumers, we often encounter claims made by statistical studies. The media frequently report such claims; we find them in newspapers, at various Web sites, on television, in magazines, and so on. We all need to be equipped to analyze the design of statistical studies and closely examine and critique the scope of inference that is allowable in any statistical study. The tasks in this chapter help students learn to approach the claims based on such studies with a healthy skepticism.

The Context

In this investigation, students' reasoning and sense making are focused on the results of a statistical study that appeared in a journal of the American Heart Association. Two excerpts from the original release to the media are provided from this study. The two media clippings reach very different conclusions about the data that the study produced. This investigation is intended to raise students' awareness about issues in the conduct of statistical studies and about what actually gets reported in the media about statistical studies. Students are asked to analyze and critique the information provided about the study in the media excerpts and then to draw their own conclusions and support them with evidence from the study.

Type of Investigation and Habits of Mind

Data from statistical studies, and particularly data from medical studies, are constantly being reported in the media—in newspapers, magazines, and television reports, as well as on many Web sites. We all need to be able to read reports of statistical studies with a critical eye—determining what can reasonably be concluded, what limitations there might be in the studies, and what conclusions, if any, seem to go beyond what the data suggest. We need to be able to question the source of the data and the methods and procedures of the study, as well as to critique the analysis and conclusions of the researchers. Thus, we—and our students—should be able to read reports of statistical research with a disposition to raise questions and maintain a healthy skepticism. Table 6.1 identifies the key element and summarizes the general reasoning habits and specific statistical reasoning habits of mind that working with the soft drinks and heart disease investigation promotes in students.

Table 6.1
Key Element and Habits of Mind in the Soft Drinks and Heart Disease Study

Key Element: Interpreting Designed Statistical Studies

Habits of Mind

Analyzing a problem

Looking for patterns and relationships by—
- analyzing and explaining variation;
- making preliminary deductions and conjectures.

Implementing a Strategy

Selecting representations or procedures by—
- choosing and critiquing data collection strategies based on the question;
- considering the random mechanisms behind the data;
- drawing conclusions beyond the data.

Monitoring one's progress

Evaluating a chosen strategy by—
- questioning whether the observations make sense within the problem context;
- evaluating the consistency of different components of the analysis.

Seeking and using connections

Connecting different representations by—
- understanding the sensitivity of an analysis to various components;
- connecting conclusions and interpretations to the context.

Reflecting on one's solutions

Checking the reasonableness of an answer by—
- considering and evaluating alternative explanations;
- understanding the allowable scope of conclusions;
- determining whether a conclusion based on the data is plausible.

The Big Statistical Ideas

The main statistical ideas in this investigation involve questioning aspects of data production and the procedures and design of a statistical study. We want our students to be capable of identifying potential problem areas in a study, to be able to point to its potential limitations, and to raise clarifying questions about the statistical claims based on it. For example, students should be able to pose questions like the following: Were the data gathered in a clear and reliable way that would be replicable by other investigators? Were the data gathered in such a way as to ensure that a *representative* sample was obtained? Do we have sufficient confidence that we could make inferences from the sample in this study to a larger population? Why, or why not? Are there any concerns that we might have about the design of the study itself, or any aspects of the procedures that we think could have influenced the outcomes one way or the other? The goal, then, is to foster in our students the skills of a statistical critic. Students need to be able to recognize both carefully conducted, high-quality statistical studies and those that could be fatally flawed.

In the Classroom

In small groups, students will generate lists of "I notice that" and "I wonder about" items from the media clips presented from this study. After the groups have shared their "notices" and "wonders," each group will discuss and critique the study, and then each will present its own conclusions based on the information provided about the study.

> ## Note to Teachers
>
> *"Notices" and "wonders" are good tools to get students engaged in looking more closely at data and statistical claims. "Notices" are observations that are fairly evident from the data or the claims made by a statistical study. However, "notices" can also lead to questions: "I notice that..., and that made me wonder about...." The process of asking students to makes lists of "notices" and "wonders" is one way to help catalyze the process of critical thinking.*

The data: Media clips and an online poll

Two clips from a recent CNN story offer opposite interpretations of the results of a study on the potential connection between soft drink consumption and the incidence of heart disease. The media clips are presented below. A subsequent poll of public reactions to this study was conducted by AOL, and the results of that poll are included with the media clips for the students' consideration. The students' task is to analyze and critique the study, to draw their own conclusions, and to defend those conclusions on the basis of the data in the clips and the poll.

Diet, sugary sodas alike linked to heart disease factors

Source: http://www.cnn.com/2007/HEALTH/conditions/07/24/diet.sodas/index.html

Media clip 1

People who drink one or more soft drinks a day have a more than 50% higher risk of developing the heart disease precursor metabolic syndrome than people who drink less than one soda a day, a new study has found. And it didn't matter if it was a regular soda or a diet soda.

Metabolic syndrome is a constellation of health problems—high waist circumference, high blood pressure, low levels of "good" cholesterol, and other health problems—that have been strongly linked to developing heart disease, stroke, and diabetes.

The study, in the American Heart Association journal *Circulation,* looked at more than 6,000 healthy people, who showed no signs of metabolic syndrome, and then followed up. After four years, 53% of people who drank an average of one or more soft drinks per day developed metabolic syndrome. Those who drank one or more diet soft drinks a day were at a 44% higher risk.

"The point is that the risk is high no matter how many soft drinks one consumes and no matter what type of soft drink one consumes," said Dr. Ramachandran S. Vasan, one of the study authors.

Conclusion 1: *People who drink soft drinks at a rate of at least one a day are at a high degree of risk for developing metabolic syndrome linked to heart disease, stroke, and diabetes.*

Media clip 2

The American Beverage Association took issue with the study, saying that the study proves no link between soft drinks and increased risk of heart disease.

The ABA added, "The assertions made could apply to any caloric product—if you over-consume any food or beverage with calories, there are health consequences." ABA also said that it is "scientifically implausible" that diet soft drinks, which have no calories, cause weight gain or elevated blood pressure.

Conclusion 2: *There is no real evidence that consuming soft drinks causes heart disease.*

A Subsequent Poll of the Readers

In conjunction with this study, AOL maintained an ongoing online poll of readers' responses to the following question:

Will you stop drinking diet soda because of this study?

Table 6.2 shows the results of the poll after three days.

Table 6.2.
Responses to the Question, "Will You Stop Drinking Diet Soda Because of This Study?"

Response	Frequency	Percent
No	15,718	52%
I don't drink diet soda	8,224	27%
Yes	6,531	21%
Total votes	30,473	100%

Summary of the task, and the statistical question

The goal of this data exploration is for students to write a short analysis and critique of this study. Students are asked to take a stand one way or another and defend it on the basis of the data. Do they agree with either of the two conclusions? If so, why? If not, why? Would they stop drinking diet soda because of this study? Why, or why not?

Note to Teachers

An effective way to implement the investigation with students is in three separate stages:

I. Notices and wonders about the clips

II. A deeper analysis and critique of the clips

III. A "reflect back" consideration of what constitutes a good statistical study.

The heart disease and soda task for students

Assign your students to small groups, and give them the following instructions:

I. Notices and wonders—Directions

First, working individually, read the two media clips and the results of the AOL poll of readers based on this study. After you have read all the information, start recording items in two lists, one headed "I Notice That…," and the other headed "I Wonder About…." Then reread the media clips and jot down any "notices" and/or "wonders" that strike you about the information presented, the way in which the study was conducted, and the conclusions from the study. Be prepared to share your notices and wonders with the other members of your group.

Next, working as a group, allow each member to share his or her notices and wonders with the other group members. For this sharing, use a "go around until" protocol, where each group member shares *one* notice or wonder from his or her list, and then the next group member takes a turn. (That way everyone has a chance to share something that they saw or questioned in the study.) Continue until all notices and wonders have been shared. One group member should be the recorder for this process, keeping a master list of all the notices and wonders.

In whole-class sharing, round 1, allow each group to share its list of notices and wonders; these items might be posted around the room or shared by means of a projection device.

> ### Note to Teachers
> *You might have your students share "notices" and "wonders" on butcher paper and post them around the room. Or these items could be shared under a document camera. Groups could share one notice and one wonder at a time, group by group, so that each group would have a chance to present something. The groups might share notices that completely contradict one another. Students could address those contradictions later, during the analysis and discussion—at this point everything should be put on the lists.*

II. Analysis and critique of study—Directions

Back in groups, through group discussion, prepare a brief written analysis and critique of the study for the group. Come to a consensus conclusion and be ready to defend it on the basis of the data. Your group might agree with claim 1, claim 2, or a different conclusion that you reach together, but whatever your conclusion is, be prepared to defend it on the basis of the data. As part of this process, decide what conclusion you would draw about the impact of this study on public opinion, as reported in the poll. Would you stop drinking diet soda because of this study?

In whole-class sharing, round 2, allow each group to present its written analysis, critique, and conclusions based on this study. Groups will make oral presentations to the entire class, and written critiques can be posted around the room afterward.

In whole-class discussion, raise questions and/or ask for clarification about other groups' presentations and conclusions.

> ### Note to Teachers
> *Just as the two media claims contradict each other, your students' group analyses and conclusions may also be at odds. Let all groups have a chance to report their analyses and conclusions before any group questions another group's analysis.*

III. Reflect back—What makes a good study?

For reflection and final discussion, take some private think time, and jot down things that you believe are important for a statistical study to include when the study is reported to the public. Share your ideas in a whole-class discussion while a class member or the teacher makes a list of everyone's ideas of what should be included in a report of a statistical study.

Examples of students' reasoning at each stage of the investigation

The following examples reflect actual reasoning and sense making of students as they work through the three stages of the investigation in their classroom.

I. Notices and wonders—Examples of students' lists

Table 6.3 illustrates the types of "notices" and "wonders" that students generate as they read the media clips.

Table 6.3
Examples of Student Notices and Wonders

I notice that...	I wonder about...
• Regular soft drinks were worse than diet drinks. • Nobody had the syndrome before the study started. • A lot of people said they would stop drinking soda because of this study. • Only 21% of people in the poll said they would stop drinking diet soda. • These clips don't tell us what kind of soda. • It isn't much difference between 53% and 44%, and both are about half. • About half the soda drinkers didn't develop the syndrome. • The study didn't report any people who drank both diet and regular sodas. • The study makes you feel that it's dangerous to drink soda. • Over 30,000 people responded to the poll; that's a lot. • The American Beverage Association seems to be saying that more than one diet drink a day is "over-consuming."	• What were the percentages of the syndrome for people who drank less than one soft drink a day after four years? • What does "44% more likely" mean? Is that like the 53%, meaning 44% of the diet drinkers had the syndrome? • Where did these 6000 people come from? • Is it a random sample of 6000, and if so, drawn from what group of people? • What else were these people eating or drinking? • Why did the poll just ask about diet soda; why not regular, too? • How reliable is people's reporting of their soft drink consumption—would they remember? Did the study ask people to keep track? • Who are the people who responded to the poll? Do we know anything about them? • Is the American Heart Association saying that soft drinks cause these diseases?

II. Analysis and critique of study—Examples of group work

The examples that follow show typical reasoning of students in groups as they defend the conclusions that they have drawn from the data and explain whether or not they would stop drinking soft drinks on the basis of the study.

Group A: We agree with the American Heart Association's conclusion. This study presents strong evidence that drinking soft drinks is likely to lead to heart disease or stroke. The regular soda drinkers are 53% more likely to develop the metabolic syndrome, and the diet drinkers are 44% more likely. The results of the poll show that only 21% of people will stop drinking soft drinks, so we feel it is very important for the results of this study to be broadcast more widely, on TV and radio news, because they are alarming, and more people need to know the dangers of drinking soft drinks.

Group B: We are leaning toward agreeing with the conclusion of the American Heart Association. The study suggests that consumption of soft drinks leads to heart disease and strokes. However, we wonder where the 44% came from. Does that mean that people were "at 44% higher risk?" Does that mean the same as the 53% number for regular drinks—53% of the soda drinkers, so, 44% of the diet soda drinkers? We wonder if the media left out or confused some details of the information, because of the way they reported it. We don't think anyone should stop drinking soda just on the basis of this media report alone. If we could get more details on the original study itself to answer some of our questions, we might be able to come to some sort of conclusion. But on the basis of these short media clips, we can't decide anything. The poll bothers us because people may change their drinking habits if they read this report, and the report has too much missing in it.

Group C: We agree with the American Beverage Association. We think 53% isn't all that much higher than 50%, which is about even up, so we don't think this study proved anything. It could just be that the result is due to random variation in that sample of 6000 people. It seems like your chances of developing this syndrome after four years are 50-50 if you drink soft drinks. And how can we be sure that people accurately remember how many soft drinks they drank over a four-year period—there's not a lot of difference between more than one or less than one a day. We're concerned that people will rush out and stop drinking soft drinks just because of something that could be totally due to chance.

Group D: In the class list of notices and wonders, there were a lot of wonders about who the 6000 people were, where they were from, how they were selected, what their medical background was—how do we know it's just the soft drinks that are involved in creating this medical syndrome? It could be other things beside soft drinks. We don't agree with either of the claims. If the 6000 people were not randomly selected, and if they weren't all medically "the same" at the beginning of the study, then how can the American Heart Association claim increased risk from drinking the soft drinks? On the other hand, the American Beverage Association doesn't have clear information that soft drinks don't cause harm either, so they have to be careful what they claim, too.

Group E: We, too, want more details about this study. What questions did they ask those 6000 people? How were people asked to estimate the number of soft drinks they had over the four-year period? We think that one of the problems with media reports is that they just leave too much information out. They are for public consumption, and maybe there is a tendency for the reporters to include only the parts that sensationalize the situation—because they want to sell news—and so they leave out some of the important scientific details. We would really like to get our hands on the details of the original study.

Group *F:* For now, we totally agree with the American Beverage Association that there is no reliable evidence at all that the soft drinks are what led to the syndrome. Just think about what folks might be eating along with their sodas. Could it be that they are consuming a double-hipped machoburger along with their soda? There isn't clear evidence of cause for heart disease, because the increase in heart disease could be due to all kinds of other variables, especially eating fatty foods along with the soda. The opinion poll is not a random sample of soft drink consumers, so it doesn't give us a good basis for predicting the soft drink behavior of that whole group. It only tells us about those who responded to the poll. We think this study raises some questions that need to be pursued in a more carefully designed study.

> **Note to Teachers**
>
> *After all the groups have presented their thinking, you might wish to encourage groups to raise questions about any other groups' analysis and conclusions. A healthy discussion could help clarify some of the reasoning and sense making issues that members of the groups were wrestling with in their analysis. At the end of the discussion, move on to the third stage of the investigation, in which students take time to jot down what they feel is important to include both in a statistical study and in a report to the public of a statistical study.*

III. Reflect back—What makes a good study? Examples of students' reflections

Students typically suggested that a statistical study should do the following:

- Indicate how the participants were selected—was the sample randomly selected, was it a convenience sample, or was some other selection mechanism used?
- Provide some background on the participants.
- Carefully explain the meaning of any numbers or percentages reported.
- Be open and honest about other potential variables that could have influenced the results of the study—like foods that accompany sodas, in the case of the study of soft drinks and heart disease.
- Explain the mechanisms for any polling that was done and describe the people who would be likely to respond to the poll—was the poll random, or just convenience, or did only a particular segment of the total population even have access to the poll?
- Suggest what the next steps should be in the research—in the case of this report, a randomized design that controls for other food and beverage variables and compares soda-drinking groups to non-soda-drinking groups to reach any conclusions about actual causes of metabolic syndrome.

Conclusion and Next Steps: Where to Go from Here

The two extensions suggested below can help students develop their reasoning about statistical studies.

Extension task 1

Students might wish to obtain the entire original report of this study. They can find it in the online edition of the American Heart Association journal *Circulation,* at http://circ.ahajournals.org/cgi/content/full/116/23/e557. The students could analyze the original report and see if any of the questions that they raised were addressed in the report but omitted in the media clip. (Note that the report includes some parts that are quite technical.) Do students still have concerns or questions that they feel were not addressed in the original report?

Note to Teachers

The original report of the study in the journal Circulation *identified "limitations" and included the following note:*

> *Given the observational nature of the present study, we cannot infer that the observed associations are causal. As noted above, it is conceivable that residual confounding by lifestyle/dietary factors not adjusted for may have contributed to the metabolic risks associated with soft drink intake. Finally, participants in the present study were all white Americans, which may limit the generalizability of our results to nonwhites.*

These acknowledged limitations are examples of what can be "left out" in the condensed versions of studies that are reported in the media. Media reports are distillations of studies, and neither of the media clips referred to these details at all. Thus, it is all the more critical to work with students to sharpen their reasoning and sense making abilities about statistical reports that appear in the media. The devil is always in the details in statistical studies!

Extension task 2

This investigation is intended to raise students' awareness about issues in the conduct of statistical studies and what gets reported in the media about statistical studies. Students can be asked to watch for statistical reports in the media. They can bring examples of clippings or Web reports to class to share their questions about the studies with their classmates. This can be an ongoing reasoning and sense making activity over an entire semester, during which students hone their skills as "data detectives." The tendency can be for students to focus only on reports that have a lot of flaws, so encourage students to try to find examples of statistical reports that have some good qualities, too.

A Reflective Look Back for Teachers

As you focus on reasoning and sense making with your students, you may find it helpful to jot down your observations and reflections in a journal. These can include questions that you have about your students' reasoning as well as thoughts on what you might do differently the next time you use the investigation with students to push them in their reasoning. In particular, for the heart disease and soda investigation, you might consider recording your ideas in response to the following questions:

1. What did you learn about your students' reasoning and sense making as they analyzed and discussed the media clips in this activity? Did anything happen that you expected? Did anything happen that surprised you?

2. Where in your curriculum or your school setting do your students have an opportunity to analyze statistical reports or statistical studies as reported in the media? Where could you make opportunities for them to do so?

3. Summarize how you might do things if you were to provide your students with another opportunity to analyze a statistical study or to critique a study as reported in the media. What would you retain from the investigation as developed in this chapter? What would you change, and how would you change it?

Appendix

NCTM Standards and Expectations for Grades 9–12

Data Analysis and Probability Standard

Instructional programs from prekindergarten through grade 12 should enable all students to—	Grades 9–12 Expectations In grades 9–12 all students should—
Formulate questions that can be addressed with data and collect, organize, and display relevant data to answer them	• understand the differences among various kinds of studies and which types of inferences can legitimately be drawn from each; • know the characteristics of well-designed studies, including the role of randomization in surveys and experiments; • understand the meaning of measurement data and categorical data, of univariate and bivariate data, and of the term *variable*; • understand histograms, parallel box plots, and scatterplots and use them to display data; • compute basic statistics and understand the distinction between a statistic and a parameter.
Select and use appropriate statistical methods to analyze data	• for univariate measurement data, be able to display the distribution, describe its shape, and select and calculate summary statistics; • for bivariate measurement data, be able to display a scatterplot, describe its shape, and determine regression coefficients, regression equations, and correlation coefficients using technological tools; • display and discuss bivariate data where at least one variable is categorical; • recognize how linear transformations of univariate data affect shape, center, and spread; • identify trends in bivariate data and find functions that model the data or transform the data so that they can be modeled.
Develop and evaluate inferences and predictions that are based on data	• use simulations to explore the variability of sample statistics from a known population and to construct sampling distributions; • understand how sample statistics reflect the values of population parameters and use sampling distributions as the basis for informal inference; • evaluate published reports that are based on data by examining the design of the study, the appropriateness of the data analysis, and the validity of conclusions; • understand how basic statistical techniques are used to monitor process characteristics in the workplace.
Understand and apply basic concepts of probability	• understand the concepts of sample space and probability distribution and construct sample spaces and distributions in simple cases; • use simulations to construct empirical probability distributions; • compute and interpret the expected value of random variables in simple cases; • understand the concepts of conditional probability and independent events; • understand how to compute the probability of a compound event.

Number and Operations
Standard

Instructional programs from prekindergarten through grade 12 should enable all students to—	Grades 9–12 Expectations In grades 9–12 all students should—
Understand numbers, ways of representing numbers, relationships among numbers, and number systems	• develop a deeper understanding of very large and very small numbers and of various representations of them; • compare and contrast the properties of numbers and number systems, including the rational and real numbers, and understand complex numbers as solutions to quadratic equations that do not have real solutions; • understand vectors and matrices as systems that have some of the properties of the real-number system; • use number-theory arguments to justify relationships involving whole numbers.
Understand meanings of operations and how they relate to one another	• judge the effects of such operations as multiplication, division, and computing powers and roots on the magnitudes of quantities; • develop an understanding of properties of, and representations for, the addition and multiplication of vectors and matrices; • develop an understanding of permutations and combinations as counting techniques.
Compute fluently and make reasonable estimates	• develop fluency in operations with real numbers, vectors, and matrices, using mental computation or paper-and-pencil calculations for simple cases and technology for more complicated cases; • judge the reasonableness of numerical computations and their results.

Measurement
Standard

Instructional programs from prekindergarten through grade 12 should enable all students to—	Grades 9–12 Expectations In grades 9–12 all students should—
Understand measurable attributes of objects and the units, systems, and processes of measurement	• make decisions about units and scales that are appropriate for problem situations involving measurement.
Apply appropriate techniques, tools, and formulas to determine measurements	• analyze precision, accuracy, and approximate error in measurement situations; • understand and use formulas for the area, surface area, and volume of geometric figures, including cones, spheres, and cylinders; • apply informal concepts of successive approximation, upper and lower bounds, and limit in measurement situations; • use unit analysis to check measurement computations.

References

American Diploma Project 2004. http://www.achieve.org.

Burrill, Gail F., and Patrick W. Hopfensperger. *Exploring Systems of Equations and Inequalities.* Data-Driven Mathematics. Parsippany, N.J.: Dale Seymour Publications, 1999.

Cobb, George W., and David S. Moore. "Mathematics, Statistics, and Teaching." *American Mathematical Monthly* 104 (November 1997): 801–23.

Franklin, Christine, Gary Kadar, Denise Mewborn, Jerry Moreno, Roxy Peck, Mike Perry, and Richard Scheaffer. *Guidelines for Assessment and Instruction in Statistics Education* (GAISE Report). Alexandria, Va.: American Statistical Association, 2005.

Frankcom, Gillian. "Statistics Teaching and Learning: The New Zealand Experience." *Proceedings of the Eleventh International Congress on Mathematics Education* (ICME 11). Monterrey, Mexico, 2008. http://tsg.icme11.org/document/get/489.

Hand, D. J., F. Daly, A. D. Lunn, K. J. McConway, and E. Ostrowski. *Handbook of Small Data Sets.* London: Chapman and Hall, 1994.

National Council of Teachers of Mathematics (NCTM). *Curriculum and Evaluation Standards for School Mathematics.* Reston, Va.: NCTM, 1989.

———. *Principles and Standards for School Mathematics.* Reston, Va.: NCTM, 2000.

———. *Curriculum Focal Points for Prekindergarten through Grade 8 Mathematics: A Quest for Coherence.* Reston, Va.: NCTM, 2006.

———. *Mathematics Teaching Today.* Reston, Va.: NCTM, 2007.

———. *Focus in High School Mathematics: Reasoning and Sense Making.* Reston, Va.: NCTM, 2009.

Shaughnessy, J. Michael, Gloria Barrett, Rick Billstein, Henry A. Kranendonk, and Roxy Peck. *Navigating through Probability in Grades 9–12. Principles and Standards for School Mathematics* Navigations Series. Reston, Va.: National Council of Teachers of Mathematics, 2004.

Shaughnessy, J. Michael, and Maxine Pfannkuch. "How Faithful Is Old Faithful? Statistical Thinking: A Story of Variation and Prediction." *Mathematics Teacher* 95 (April 2002): 252–59.

Wild, Chris J., and Maxine Pfannkuch. "Statistical Thinking in Empirical Inquiry." *International Statistical Review* 67 (December 1999): 223–65.